MÅRBACKA

THE WORKS OF
SELMA LAGERLÖF

Translated from Swedish by
VELMA SWANSTON HOWARD
JERUSALEM, A Novel
THE HOLY CITY, JERUSALEM II
WONDERFUL ADVENTURES OF NILS
FURTHER ADVENTURES OF NILS
GIRL FROM THE MARSH CROFT
LEGEND OF THE SACRED IMAGE
THE EMPEROR OF PORTUGALLIA
MÅRBACKA
CHARLOTTE LÖWENSKÖLD
ANNA SVÄRD
MEMORIES OF MY CHILDHOOD
CHRIST LEGENDS

Translated from Swedish by
PAULINE BANCROFT FLACH
MIRACLES OF ANTICHRIST
STORY OF GÖSTA BERLING
INVISIBLE LINKS

Translated from Swedish by
JESSIE BROCHNER
FROM A SWEDISH HOMESTEAD

Translated from Swedish by
ANNA BARWELL
LILLIECRONA'S HOME

Translated from Swedish by
W. WORSTER, M. A.
THE OUTCAST

Translated from Swedish by
ARTHUR G. CHATER
THE TREASURE

Translated from Swedish by
FRANCESCA MARTIN
THE GENERAL'S RING

MÅRBACKA

SELMA LAGERLÖF

TRANSLATED BY
VELMA SWANSTON HOWARD

DOUBLEDAY, DORAN & COMPANY, INC.
NEW YORK 1938

MJ167

CONTENTS

The Strömstad Journey

The Old Housekeeper's Tales

CONTENTS

OLD HOUSES AND OLD PEOPLE

THE NEW MÅRBACKA

WORKDAYS AND FÊTE DAYS

THE STRÖMSTAD JOURNEY

MÅRBACKA

I

THE NURSEMAID

ONCE they had a nursemaid at Mårbacka who was called Back-Kaisa. She must have been all of six feet high. She had a large-featured, swarthy, stern-looking face, her hands were hard and full of cracks, in which the children's hair would catch when she combed it, and she was heavy and mournful.

A person of that sort could hardly be said to have been especially created for the nursery, and indeed Fru Lagerlöf had deliberated a long while before engaging her. The girl had never been out to service and knew nothing of the ways of people; she had grown up on a poor backwoods croft, among the wooded hills above Mårbacka, far from any other habitation.

Probably there was no one else available, or Fru Lagerlöf would not have had her come. That the girl did not know how to make up a bed, or build a fire in a tile-stove, or prepare a bath, was understood beforehand; but she was teachable and did not mind sweeping out the nursery every day, or dusting, or washing baby-clothes. What she could not seem to learn, however, was how to get along with the little folk. She never played with them or gave them a pleasant word. She knew no sagas and no songs. It was not that she meant to be unkind, but she was so constituted that romp and frolic and laughter were hateful to her. She would have liked the children to sit quietly, each in his or her little chair, without moving or talking.

Fru Lagerlöf was at all events quite pleased with the nursemaid. As for her not knowing any stories—well, the Mårbacka children had their grandmother, who every morning as soon as she was dressed gathered the youngsters about her, and sang and narrated for them till away up to dinner-time. And they had someone, too, who played with them, for Lieutenant Lagerlöf, whenever he had a spare moment, romped with his children.

Back-Kaisa was strong, patient, and dutiful. She was a person to be depended on. When her master and mistress went off to a party, they could rest assured that she did not run out and leave the children alone in the nursery. If only she'd had a more delicate touch she would have been admirable. But hers were no gentle clutches when little arms had to go into dress-sleeves. When she washed the children the soap always got into their eyes; and when she wielded the comb they felt as if every wisp of hair were being torn from their heads.

The nursery at Mårbacka was a light, warm, spacious

room—the best in the whole house. But, unhappily, it was a gable-room, and to get there one had first to go out into the lower front hall, then up a flight of steps and across a big attic. The attic stairs were steep, and difficult for little feet to climb. Now the former nursemaid used to take a child on her arm and carry it up, but Back-Kaisa didn't seem to know enough for that. And it was positively terrifying to walk the length of that attic—above all, after dark! So it seemed almost necessary that little hands should have a large hand to slip into. But Back-Kaisa, who had been accustomed to the dark of the wild forest, probably thought the attic at Mårbacka a nice safe place. She just stalked on and never so much as put out a hand. One was glad if one could even catch hold of a corner of her skirt.

The beds in which the three children slept had been made by the clever old carpenter at Askersby, and they were quite decorative, with a little row of spindles across each headboard; but they were in two sections that pulled out and pushed in like a drawer. Large as the nursery was, the three beds when open took up a lot of space; so it was well they could be folded during the day. Now that in itself was all right, but the clever old carpenter had somehow managed to make the beds in such a way that they sometimes sprang apart in the dead of the night.

When that happened, you were of course startled out of your sweetest slumber. Finding your bed cut off in the middle, you drew yourself into the upper end and tried to catch back sleep again. But somehow it would not come. After a while you stretched out your legs and let them dangle. In that position you lay waiting for the Sandman till you were as wide awake as in broad day. Then at last you decided to get up and try to push the two parts together. When you had apparently succeeded and had got the bedclothes nicely straightened, you crept back into bed as cautiously as possible, and stretched out once more with a feeling of satisfaction. All went well, sleep came stealing on, then a careless turn and—crickety-crash!—the bed was apart again . . . which put an end to all hope of getting any sleep that night.

But Back-Kaisa slept peacefully through it all. It did not occur to any of the little ones that they might awaken her and ask for help. The former nursemaid had always jumped up the instant a bed broke down, and quickly fixed it without having to be asked.

Just over the nursery there was a little lumber-loft full of discarded looms and spinning-wheels, and amid all that old rubbish lived an owl.

At night that owl made a dreadful racket. To the children's ears it sounded as if someone were rolling big, heavy logs over their heads. The former nursemaid used to laugh at them when they were frightened by the noise, and say there was nothing to be scared about—it was only the owl. But Back-Kaisa, who hailed from the forest, was afraid of all animals, furred and feathered.

They were to her like evil spirits. So, whenever she was awakened in the night by the owl she would take out her prayer book and begin to read. Indeed she could not soothe the children; on the contrary, she terrified them so that the poor little owl grew into a huge monster with tiger-claws and eagle-wings. No words can picture how they lay shuddering to the very roots of their being at the thought of having a horrible ogre like that right above them. What if it should tear a hole through the ceiling with its great claws, and come swooping down . . . !

It can never be said of Back-Kaisa that she neglected the children, or beat them. But was that anything much? True, the former nursemaid had not been so particular about keeping them neat and clean; but she was oh, so good to them!

The children had three little wooden chairs which they regarded as their greatest treasure. These had been presented to them by the clever old carpenter of Askersby. Whether they were meant as compensation for his failure with the beds, they did not know, but they rather thought so. At any rate, the chairs were not failures. They were both light and strong, and could be used as tables and sleds. The children could ride them all around the room, stand upon them and jump to the floor, or lay them down and play they were a cow shed, a stable, or a rabbit hutch. Oh, there was nothing they could not be used for!

Why the children prized those chairs so highly could

be seen at a glance by turning them upside down. On
the bottom of each chair was the portrait of its owner.
On one was Johan, a boy in blue with a long riding whip
in his hand; on another posed Anna, a dainty little maid
in a red frock and yellow leghorn hat—sniffing at a nose-
gay; while on the third was Selma, a tiny tot in a blue
dress and striped apron, but with nothing in her hand
and nothing on her head.

Now these portraits had been painted there to show
to whom the chairs belonged, and the children regarded
them as their property in quite a different sense from
wearing apparel and other things they received from
their parents. Their clothes travelled from one to
another, and their nice toys were either locked away or
set up on the corner bracket in the parlour; but the chairs,
which bore their likenesses—who would have thought
of depriving them of these?

Therefore, it was awfully mean of Back-Kaisa to put
all three chairs on top of the high birch-wood bureau,
as she did sometimes, so that the children could not
get at them. What if she had but just scrubbed the
nursery and the little chairs would leave ugly marks on
the wet floor if trailed across it? The former nursemaid never would have had the heart to take the chairs
away from them. No, not even for a moment.

Fru Lagerlöf saw, to be sure, that the maid did not
understand her little ones and that they were afraid of
her. But Back-Kaisa had been hired for a year, and
Fru Lagerlöf could not very well send her away before

her time was up. She hoped, however, that things would be better in the summer, when the children could play out of doors, and have less to do with the nurse-maid.

One forenoon in the early summer, it happened that the youngest child, a little girl, had been left alone, and asleep, in the nursery. On awaking she sat up in bed, half-dazed, and wondered where everyone had gone; at the same time she felt singularly drowsy and uncomfortable. She remembered, as she came to herself somewhat, that earlier in the day she and the other children had been to Ås Springs with their father to bathe. On their return Back-Kaisa had put all three of them to bed—dressed as they were—that they might nap a while before dinner. But the beds on which Johan and Anna had lain now stood empty; so the little girl knew, of course, that they were already up and gone.

They were perhaps out in the garden playing? She felt a bit hurt at their running off like that, leaving her all by herself in the nursery. She had better crawl out of bed, she thought, and hurry down to them.

The little girl was then three and a half years old, and she could easily open the door and walk down the stairs. But to cross the dangerous attic alone . . . She listened—perhaps someone was coming to fetch her. . . . No, there were no footsteps on the stair; she would have to venture by herself.

But now that she wanted to rise from her bed she could not. She tried again and again, only to sink back. Her legs did not seem to belong to her; she had lost all control of them.

The child was terror-stricken. The feeling of utter helplessness which came over her when the body refused to obey was something so dreadful she remembered it long, long afterwards—aye, all her life.

Naturally, she began to cry. She was in great trouble, and there was no grown person at hand to help or comfort her. But she had not been alone such a very long while when the door opened and Back-Kaisa appeared.

"Isn't Selma coming down to dinner? The big folk——" Back-Kaisa stopped short.

The little girl never thought about its being the cross nursemaid who stood in the doorway. In her desperate plight she only saw a grown person who could help her —and put out her arms to her.

"Come and take me, Back-Kaisa!" she cried. "Come and take me!"

When the nurse came up to the bedside the little girl threw her arms about her neck and clung to her as no child had ever done before. A little tremor went through Back-Kaisa, and her voice was not real steady when she asked:

"What's the matter with Selma? Is her sick?"

"I can't walk, Back-Kaisa," wailed the child.

Then a pair of strong arms lifted her up as easily as if she were just a tiny kitten, and all at once the stern, serious-minded woman knew how to talk to a little child.

"Naa—Selma mustn't cry for that! Back-Kaisa's going to carry Selma."

And with that it seemed as if all the little one's troubles had blown away. She was no longer afraid or unhappy. What did it matter that she herself could not walk when Back-Kaisa would carry her! And nobody had to tell her; she knew that one who had a good strong friend like Back-Kaisa was not so badly off after all.

II

JOHAN and Anna were driven nearly to distraction by the terrible commotion created by Selma's illness.

That one may well understand. Johan was then seven years of age, and learning to read under the tutelage of Herr Tyberg. He was a boy, of course, and almost regarded as the eldest child; though, to be sure, he had an elder brother. But the latter mostly stayed with his maternal grandparents at Filipstad, and was hardly ever at home. And now, all at once, it seemed that nobody had a thought for him—Johan—but only for the littlest girl.

As for Anna—she was five, and she could already both sew and crochet. She was pretty to look at, too, and the elder daughter, and mamma's pet. But what was the good of all that since Selma had gone and got sick?

The grown-ups, you see, were so touched by the sight of a child who could not walk. "How will the poor little thing go through life?" they would sigh.—— "She'll have to stay in the one place always, and never see anything of the world."—— "She'll never get

married and she'll never be able to support herself."——
"It's going to be cruelly hard for her, poor child."
They were all very tender and full of pity for the sick
girl. Now *that* Johan and Anna had nothing against;
but folks didn't have to forget that there were other
children.

The worst one of all, though, was Back-Kaisa. She
carried Selma on her back, prattled with her, and told
her she was a perfect little angel. And, indeed, Father
and Mother and Granny and Auntie were not much
better. Didn't the clever old carpenter at Askersby
have to make her a little wagon, so that Back-Kaisa
might draw her about? And were Johan and Anna
ever allowed to borrow that wagon to cart sand in?—
No, no! That was for Selma's use, and they mustn't
soil it.

Johan and Anna both knew that when Selma could
walk there had been nothing remarkable about her; but
now visitors couldn't come to the house but she must be
carried in for them to see and make a fuss over. And
if a peasant woman happened to drop into the kitchen
Back-Kaisa was there in a jiffy, showing Selma to her.
The exasperating thing about it all was that Back-Kaisa
was forever saying what a good child Selma was—she
never cried and never sulked, even though so helpless.
And why shouldn't she be good, thought Johan and
Anna, the way she was treated! Carried about, and
waited on, and petted, day in and day out!

Yes, Back-Kaisa was certainly very trying, Johan

and Anna agreed. She could not bear to see Fru
Lagerlöf make Anna a prettier dress than the one
Selma got; and if any one happened to say of Johan,
that he was a nice polite little boy, she'd always remark:
"'Twould be a shame for one that's able to walk, and
can go where he likes, not to be good."

That old Doctor Hedberg of Sunne was called in time
and again on Selma's account, Johan and Anna thought
no more than right; nor did they complain when Högman's Inga, who often came to the manor to mumble
over sick cows and pigs, was consulted. But they felt
it had gone rather far when once, in the absence of
Lieutenant Lagerlöf, Back-Kaisa and Granny and the
housekeeper put their heads together, and sent for the
dangerous old witch-doctor of Högbergssäter—she
who every Maundy Thursday greased a broomstick
and went riding to the Witches' Kitchen. They had
heard that she had the power to set fire to a house by
just looking at it, and were dreadfully uneasy the whole
time she was at Mårbacka. They thought it very wrong
of Back-Kaisa to bring a horrid creature like her to the
house.

Of course Johan and Anna wanted to have Selma
restored to health. They above everyone wished her
well again. All the same, they didn't think it a bit
nice of her to go and catch a sickness no one could cure.
But Back-Kaisa must have thought differently. For
when neither Doctor Hedberg, who had so often cured
them of coughs and colds, nor Högman's Inga, who

never failed with cows and pigs, nor yet the dangerous witch-hag, who could put life into a broomstick, had been able to help her, Back-Kaisa vowed she was growing more and more wonderful all the time. And when Lieutenant Lagerlöf finally took her to Karlstad and showed her to Surgeon Major Haak, who was the best doctor in the city, and even he could do nothing for her, then Back-Kaisa was ready to burst with pride. Now wouldn't it have been better if Selma had taken on a sickness that would come to an end? So at least thought Johan and Anna.

The worst of it was that Selma was getting quite spoiled by Back-Kaisa's being too good to her. Little as she was, she had found out that it was not necessary for her to be as obedient as the other children, who could stand on their feet. Above all, she did not have to eat food that was not to her liking. When Fru Lagerlöf set before her a helping of stewed carrots, or spinach, or some hard-boiled eggs, or a plate of ale-soup, she was not expected to finish her portion as in other days; she had only to push her plate away, and immediately Back-Kaisa ran out to the kitchen and fetched something Selma liked.

And it was not enough with that!—Johan and Anna noticed that when Doctor Hedberg and Högman's Inga and the old witch had all failed to cure her, Selma thought herself too grand to eat plain fare. Why, she barely deigned to touch fried chicken and new potatoes and wild strawberries and cream. But when she had been to Karlstad, and the great Doctor Haak had said he could do nothing for her, then she would not eat anything but pastry and preserves.

Johan and Anna had heard that Aunt Nana Hammargren, who lived in Karlstad, was dreadfully worried about Selma, and feared she would starve to death; and they, too, felt that unless something happened very soon to change all this, it might end badly.

But something did happen.

One morning Back-Kaisa carried the little girl into the kitchen-bedroom and set her down among the pillows on Grandmother Lagerlöf's big white bed.

"Now Selma's going to see something," she said.

The bed was made up—sheets and all—but it had not been slept in during the night, and apparently no one lay there now, either. Grandmother Lagerlöf, who was not usually up at that early hour, sat all dressed on the corner sofa; and Aunt Lovisa, who shared the kitchen-bedroom, was also up and dressed. They both looked happy and content, and when the little girl was well seated on the bed they arose and went over to her.

"Aha! Grand company came last night," her grandmother said with a chuckle.

The little girl laughed, too, for what could be more delightful than having visitors in the house! She looked up and down and all around, wondering where the grand company might be. It was nowhere in the room, surely—not in the yellow corner-cupboard, nor behind the tall grandfather's clock, nor under Auntie's chiffonier. There was only one good hiding-place— the covered passage leading to the cellar; but the grand company could never have crawled in there.

It was all very strange! Why was she sitting on Granny's bed, and why were the others standing there staring, as if the grand company were in the bed? She glanced from one to the other, quite bewildered. Presently Aunt Lovisa bent down and moved the pillows a little. Then Selma saw that by her side lay a small oblong bundle, to which she attached no importance whatever. Granny had said that grand company had come, and grand company meant only one thing— far-come visitors who brought toys and big bags of candy for the children. That was the company she was looking for.

"Are they in there?" she asked, pointing toward the parlour. She listened for the sound of voices from the next room; seeing how pleased and elated the others were, her expectations rose high.

"Why, she's right there beside you." Granny lifted a corner of the oblong bundle and revealed two tiny hands and a little wizened face.

The little girl gave the swaddling a scornful glance then looked away. She had seen such before, and did not care for them. Her thoughts were on the company with the candy bags.

"See," said Aunt Lovisa, "this is a little sister who came to you last night, and you must be good to her."

Here was something for which she was wholly un-
prepared. She would have been glad to welcome
another sister—one who could walk and talk; but this
swaddling did not interest her at all.

However, it was plain to her now that no grand company had come. Granny meant only the poor little baby,
and she knew very well that *it* had not brought any
candy.

She felt so bitterly disappointed that she just had to
cry. Back-Kaisa was obliged to carry her out to the
kitchen, lest her crying awaken the grand company.

And she had cause for tears. Her day of power and
supremacy was over. Back-Kaisa had now to help
Fru Lagerlöf with the care of the little newcomer, who
was even more helpless and lost, as it were, than Selma.
One couldn't reason with the baby, so it was always
she, Selma, who had to be patient, and wait.

From that time on they were not so keen about
showing her to company. Now it was the swaddling
that was brought forward to be seen and praised. All
the glamour and greatness had dropped from her; she
was no more now than Anna or Johan.

The year that followed she had many distressing
experiences. She had not only to give up living ex-
clusively on a diet of pastry and preserves, but things
even went so far that when Fru Lagerlöf served her
boiled carrots, or spinach, or pease-pods, no one removed her plate and brought her other fare. She had
to eat what was set before her. If Anna received a

prettier dress than Selma no one protested. On the contrary, they all thought it only fair, since Anna was the eldest daughter.

Ah, sometimes her heart sank way down into her boots, for she was not altogether certain that Back-Kaisa did not care just as much for the wee one as she did for her.

III

BACK-KAISA and her charge were on a journey. They sat perched up on the box of the big close-carriage with Magnus, the coachman, who was so gripped by his responsibility of driving three horses on the dreadful road to Karlstad that not a word could be got out of him.

On the back seat of the carriage sat Fru Lagerlöf and Mamselle Lovisa, with Johan and Anna opposite, their backs to the horses. It was much more fun, of course, to sit on the coach-box and watch the horses than being shut in under the tilt. Johan would have liked to be up there with Magnus; but Fru Lagerlöf had said it was impossible to squeeze Back-Kaisa in on the front seat, and where she rode, Selma must ride. Lieutenant Lagerlöf was also along on the journey, but he rode alone at some distance ahead, in his carriole.

It was a year now since the little girl first lost the use of her legs, and in all that time she had not set foot on the ground. She was now being taken to the West Coast in the hope that the sea air and the baths might possibly effect a cure. She was the only invalid among

18

them, but a summer at the seaside would no doubt be of benefit to all.

The little girl sitting up there on the driver's seat had quite forgotten her affliction. She and Back-Kaisa were going away together, and the baby had been left at home! She was looking forward to a revival of those happy, never-to-be-forgotten times.

Snuggling close to the nurse, she put her arms about her neck and asked her again and again if she was not glad that they two could now be together, with no one to disturb them.

There was no reply. But the little girl did not much mind; Back-Kaisa had never been a talking person.

The great highroad to Karlstad was just one hill after another. There was the tortuous stretch round Bävik and Gunnarsby Hill, which was about three and a half English miles long; then came the steep grade up to the Sundgård mountains which was close to vertical. But most perilous of all was Kleva towering above an abyss. It was up and down the whole time, as if one were see-sawing between heaven and earth. Lieutenant Lagerlöf, to make the going easier, had ordered three horses put to the carriage—an arrangement to which neither horses nor driver was accustomed.

If anything was calculated to increase the little girl's delight at having Back-Kaisa all to herself once more, it was being allowed to sit where she could look down at the frisky horses that dashed on as if the heavy carriage were only a toy wagon, tearing round the curves,

with the vehicle sometimes on two wheels. Often the
horses would stiffen their legs and make the downgrade
almost on their haunches, and when they came to a
sudden drop in the road, Magnus would stand up and
use the whip desperately, to urge the horses on so
that the high carriage would not come tumbling over
them.

In the middle of one of these break-neck descents the
little girl again turned to the nurse and said:

"Aren't you glad, Back-Kaisa, to be alone with me?
Aren't you glad, Back-Kaisa, the baby isn't along?"

There came no response now, either; and wondering,
the child turned so that she could see the nurse's face.
. . . Back-Kaisa sat holding on to the seat, a
fixed stare in her eyes, her lips compressed, her face
the hue of ashes. "Isn't Back-Kaisa glad——?" But
the little girl now saw that Back-Kaisa was far from
glad and she was so crestfallen she could have cried.

Then at last Back-Kaisa spoke:

"Hush up, Selma! You must't talk when you're
facing such danger! Never've I known worse! But
for your sake, I'd 've got down and gone home long ago."

The little girl sat pondering the reply, not quite
satisfied. She was never afraid when with Back-Kaisa,
so why should Back-Kaisa be afraid when she was with
her? It was nice of her, though, not to get down and
go home; but it would have been nicer if she had felt
too happy to be scared.

IV

THE Mårbacka folk, though still on their journey, no longer sat in fear and trembling in the
jolting carriage. Now they were on board a
fine steamer called the *Uddeholm*.

They had spent the day in Karlstad, shopping and
visiting with relatives. Toward evening they left the
city and stood waiting a good while on the long pier
that shoots far out into big Lake Vänern. No shore
being visible in one direction, Back-Kaisa had at once
become alarmed; she thought that *over there* must be
the edge of the world. Wonderful to behold—for her
as for the others—was the pretty steamer as she emerged
from that "shoreless place" and came gliding toward
the pier to take them on board.

When Back-Kaisa saw how her master and mistress,
Mamselle Lovisa, Johan, and Anna all went up the
gangplank without the least hesitancy, she of course
followed, albeit reluctantly. She probably thought
Lieutenant Lagerlöf had conscience enough not to
expose his little ones deliberately to the peril of death.
But what would become of them once they reached the

world's end? That was something beyond her ken.
She would have liked to remain on deck to see whether
the water went down a chasm, or wherever it went.
But when dusk began to settle, the Mårbacka women
and children were requested to go below-decks. They
were conducted into something called a cabin, the
smallest room they had ever seen, where they arranged
themselves for the night.

On a narrow sofa that took up the whole side of one
wall, Fru Lagerlöf lay without undressing. Opposite,
on a similar sofa, was Mamselle Lovisa. Over Fru
Lagerlöf, on a sort of shelf, Johan was stowed, and Anna
occupied another shelf above Mamselle Lovisa's sofa.
On the floor, between the two sofas, with some blankets
under them, lay Back-Kaisa and Selma. Thus, every
bit of space was occupied; there was not the least little
corner where one might stand or sit.

The lights were extinguished, the good-nights said,
and everyone settled down to sleep. For a time it was
dead still in the cabin. Then, all at once, the floor
began to go up and down in the strangest way! The
little girl rolled like a ball, first over toward Fru Lagerlöf's sofa, then back toward the nurse. It was great
fun; only she could not understand why the floor did
not hold still. Presently she heard her mother and her
aunt whisper to each other.

"I must have eaten too much of that rich salmon at
the Sjöstedts'," said her mother.

"I thought at the time it was not very sensible food

they set before us," Aunt Lovisa remarked. "And they knew we were to be out on Vänern."

"No, Vänern isn't pleasant!" sighed Fru Lagerlöf. Then Back-Kaisa, too, began to whisper.

"Say, *Frua*, are we there yet?—there where the sea stops, and the water rushes down the bottomless pit?"

"My dear girl, there'll be no stop to the sea to-night!" said Fru Lagerlöf, who did not know what Back-Kaisa was talking about.

Again there was silence for a space, but not stillness. The floor rocked on and the little girl continued her delightful rolling.

Fru Lagerlöf struck a match and lit the lantern.

"I must see whether the children are able to hold themselves on their shelves," she said.

"Lord be praised for the light!" said Mamselle Lovisa. "Anyhow, there's no chance of our getting a wink of sleep to-night."

"Oh, Frua! Oh, Mamselle Lovisa! don't you feel that we're going down and down?" Back-Kaisa wailed. "Oh, how'll we ever get out of this deep? How'll we ever get back home?"

"Now, whatever does she mean?" queried Mamselle Lovisa.

"She says that we have reached the last extremity," Fru Lagerlöf interpreted—no more comprehending than the other.

The little girl had a faint suspicion that they were

uneasy. As for herself, she was exceedingly comfortable, lying as it were in a big rocking-swing.

The door-handle turned, the red hanging was swept to one side, and in the doorway stood Lieutenant Lagerlöf, chuckling.

"How is it, Gustaf?" asked Fru Lagerlöf anxiously. "Will it be a gale, do you think?"

"So you're awake, all of you," said the Lieutenant. "Ay, it has blown up a bit," he conceded in a reassuring tone. "The Captain thought I'd better come down and tell you it will be no worse than it is."

"What are you up to now?" Mamselle Lovisa asked him. "Aren't you going to bed?"

"Where do you think I should sleep, Sister dear?" And there was something so screamingly funny about him as he stood in the doorway (further he could not come), looking up and down as if in search of a sleeping place—it set them all laughing. Fru Lagerlöf and Mamselle Lovisa, who had been lying there fearful and a little seasick, now sat up in their bunks to have their laugh out. Johan and Anna laughed so hard they nearly shook themselves off their "shelves." Back-Kaisa forgot for the moment that she would soon be at that dreadful place where the lake ends, and laughed, too, and the little girl by her side was fairly choking with laughter.

Lieutenant Lagerlöf, who seldom laughed aloud, looked highly pleased.

"All's right with you, I see," he said. "So now I'll

go up again and chin with the captain." Whereupon he bade them a cheery good-night, and went his
way.

In the cabin the feeling of uneasiness and the qualms
of seasickness returned. Fru Lagerlöf again made futile
attempts to quiet Back-Kaisa, who went on moaning
and wailing that they were getting nearer and nearer
that bottomless pit. The little girl by her side must
have fallen asleep, for she remembered no more of that
night's experiences.

V

AT THE GOLDSMITH'S SHOP

THE most trying part of the journey was over. The travellers were safely landed at Göteborg, where they cast away all care and set out in the glorious summer weather to view the city.

They wandered up Östra Hamngatan. Lieutenant Lagerlöf, stick in hand, hat pushed far back on his head, spectacles drawn far down on his nose, was in the lead. Behind him walked Fru Lagerlöf, holding Johan by the hand; behind her, Mamselle Lovisa, leading Anna; and last came Back-Kaisa who carried Selma on her arm—for it would never do, she thought, to let the little girl ride pig-back in a city.

Lieutenant Lagerlöf had donned a brown coat and light straw hat. Fru Lagerlöf and Mamselle Lovisa were attired in voluminous black silk skirts and fine velvet bodices, with white inserts and wrist-ruffles, over which they wore large cashmere shawls—folded tricornerwise—that almost concealed their dresses; and they had on Panama hats with broad, floppy brims. Johan was in black velvet breeches and smock, and Anna was dressed in a stiffly starched blue polka-dot print worn over a crinoline; and she had both hat and parasol. Selma had on a dress exactly like Anna's, only she was wearing a sunbonnet instead of a hat, and had neither parasol nor crinoline.

The Lieutenant suddenly halted, turned, and looked back at his line of women and children. He nodded and smiled. It was plain he liked having them with him.

"Here none of us has ever been before," he said, "so now we'll look about."

They sauntered on up the street, now looking at the buildings, now at the canals and little bridges, at passing vehicles and promenaders, at signs and lamp-posts; but most of all, of course, they peered into shop windows.

The Lieutenant did not hurry them, he wanted them to see and enjoy as much as their eyes could take in.

"Nobody here knows us, so gaze as long as you like," said he.

Mamselle Lovisa stopped before a milliner's window, where a hat trimmed with white swansdown and pink rosebuds had caught her eye. There she stood, with Anna by the hand, as if rooted to the spot. And of course Lieutenant and Fru Lagerlöf, Johan, Back-Kaisa, and Selma were also obliged to stop before the swansdown hat. But Mamselle Lovisa was not thinking of them; she stood as in a trance. It tickled the Lieutenant to see her so carried away, though after a long, vain wait for her to "come back," so to speak, he lost patience.

"You're not thinking of copying that hat, Lovisa?"

he said. "Why, that's more suitable for a girl of seventeen."

"It may be a pleasure perhaps for one who is not so young to look at pretty things," retorted Mamselle Lovisa, who, though past her first youth, was still comely and rather elegant in her attire.

When they were well away from the swansdown hat they came to a goldsmith's shop. Now it was the Lieutenant who stopped first. As he stood feasting his eyes on the trays of sparkling rings and bracelets, shining silver spoons and goblets, and much else displayed in the window, he ejaculated innocent oaths of delight.

"Here we'll go in!" he said abruptly.

"But, Gustaf!" Fru Lagerlöf protested, "we can't be buying such things now."

She laid a restraining hand on his arm, for he had already opened the big plate-glass door of the shop and was stepping in. There was nothing for the others to do but follow. By the time they were all inside he was over at the counter talking to a young clerk.

"No, thank you, I don't wish to buy anything," he said. "But, seeing so many choice things in the window, I thought I'd just step in and ask if I might also have a peep at the fine wares you have in the shop."

The clerk looked a bit uneasy, and seemed at a loss what to reply. Fru Lagerlöf and Mamselle Lovisa now stood with their hands on the Lieutenant's shoulders, trying to drag him away.

The goldsmith himself presently emerged from an inner room. He had evidently heard them come in, and probably thought he would do a brisk trade. Placing himself beside the clerk, he put the flat of his hands on the counter and inquired invitingly what was desired.

Lieutenant Lagerlöf repeated in substance what he had said to the clerk—that he would very much like to see the beautiful wares in the place though he could not afford to purchase any.

The goldsmith cocked his head and looked at the Lieutenant out of the corner of his eye.

"The gentleman, I take it, is a Värmlander?" he said.

"Hell, yes, of course I'm a Värmlander!" the Lieutenant wagged back. "What the deuce else should I be?"

Then everybody roared. The clerks all crowded round the Lieutenant, and from the inner rooms came a finely dressed woman—the wife of the goldsmith—who wanted to know what the fun was about.

Fru Lagerlöf and Mamselle Lovisa were so mortified they could have wished themselves back in the jolting carriage on the Karlstad road, or the rocking boat on stormy Vänern—anywhere but in that fine shop!

"Come now, Gustaf," they urged, "for pity's sake let us get out of here!"

"No, no, please don't go!" begged the goldsmith in his most persuasive tone. "We should be so happy to show you what we carry here."

He gave orders to the clerks, who ran up ladders and

brought down everything from the shelves, opened
cabinets, and took out all their contents, so that the
long counter was literally covered with gold and silver-
ware. The shop-keeper and his wife took up each
article and showed it to the strangers, explaining its
workmanship and what it was for.

Lieutenant Lagerlöf drew off his spectacles and
polished the lenses with his silk handkerchief, the better
to see. He picked up heavy silver tankards and examined their ornamentations, admiring and praising
them.

"I say, Lovisa, this is worse than at the Deanery in
Sunne!" he remarked to his sister.

Another time he held a large silver salver before the
eyes of Back-Kaisa. "The Giant of Åsbergen doesn't
dine off finer plate—eh, Kaisa?" he said.

The clerks sniggered and joked among themselves,
having fun at his expense. The goldsmith and his
wife were also enjoying themselves, but in a different
way. They were friendly, and liked the Lieutenant.
It was not long before they knew who he was, and whom
he had with him; that he was on his way to Strömstad
to seek a cure for a child who had some hip trouble and
could not walk.

Fru Lagerlöf and Mamselle Lovisa, seeing that all
went well, composed themselves and began to look at
and delight in the display. Fru Lagerlöf was pleased
to find an old design in silver spoons, such as they once
had in her parental home, and Mamselle Lovisa became

quite as enraptured with a sugar bowl as she had been shortly before with the swansdown hat.

When they had finally seen enough and were saying good-bye, it seemed almost as if they were parting from old friends. The goldsmith, his wife, and all the clerks followed them out into the street. Passers-by must have thought they had made purchases amounting to thousands of kronor.

"I really must apologize," said Lieutenant Lagerlöf, putting out his hand in a final farewell.

"Don't think of it, Lieutenant!" answered the goldsmith.

"But we have put you to so much trouble," Fru Lagerlöf interpolated in a deprecating tone.

"We have had a most enjoyable hour," the goldsmith assured her, "so don't be uneasy about us! One has to do something for one's own pleasure, now and then, though one does stand in a shop."

As the Lieutenant continued his stroll up Östra Hamngatan his hat was pushed farther back on his head than usual. He flourished his cane as he stepped along, proud of his adventure.

Fru Lagerlöf said in a low voice to Mamselle Lovisa: "I can't tell you how anxious I was; I thought we would surely be thrown out."

"It would never have done for any one but Gustaf," replied Mamselle Lovisa, "but no one can resist him."

VI

GRAY ISLAND

NOW the Mårbacka folk had no anxiety in providing for the table; they had only to run out to the market and purchase whatever was needed. They were not worrying about the cows not having good pasturage, nor the oats not coming up; they lived amid barren cliffs and water, and had forgotten there were such things in the world as fields and meadows. Nor did they have to stand in a hot kitchen preparing fancy dishes for far-come guests, nor worry their heads out of joint wondering where they'd find sleeping-room and bedding enough for all. If the animals sickened or the housekeeper and the maids fell to quarrelling, they were blissfully unaware of it. They had freedom and leisure for healthful amusements, with no cares or annoyances of any sort.

Never had they led such an easy, comfortable life. Fru Lagerlöf, who had come to Strömstad rather thin and worn, took on flesh and colour. She soon looked and felt ten years younger. Mamselle Lovisa, who was quite stout and logy, and so diffident she could hardly open her mouth when among strangers, lost weight, grew better looking, and more sociable. Johan and

Anna made many friends among the little Strömstad children. Johan was quite wild about crabbing, and Anna had become so attached to two little girls, daughters of the confectioner, who were continually treating her to sweets, they both declared they never wanted to go home again.

As for the little sick girl, there had been no marked improvement; she was apparently no better or stronger. But that did not seem to trouble her. She had got her wish: Back-Kaisa and she were again inseparable friends; she could order her about and was being petted and spoiled by her just as in the first days of her illness.

But the one who had the best time was Lieutenant Lagerlöf. The first week or so he must have got many a sharp look and curt reply when he spoke to every person he met, as was his wont when walking along the road at home. But he was not daunted. It was a point of honour with him to be on friendly terms with people. Nor could the Strömstaders resist him in the long run. A smile lighted up the solemn faces of the pious women of the Schartuan sect when they passed him in the street. He had been in their cottages and drunk coffee with them, had asked after their husbands, and had praised their children. A gang of small boys tagged after him in the street, for they had discovered that he always had a pocketful of coppers. With the fishermen he was on so solid a footing that one after another asked him to go out mackerel fishing. All the

old retired sea captains, who went about at home bored
and longing to be out at sea, treated him to grog on
their little verandas, and told him of their adventures
and perils in the days when they knocked about the
world.

Lieutenant Lagerlöf liked the people, and wanted to
know how they lived their lives in their part of the
country. He was no respecter of persons, but spoke
to all, high and low, and he never lacked for topics
of conversation. Good-humoured, kindly man that
he was, it was not strange the Strömstaders liked
him. And it cannot be said that he did not know his
power.

Fortune favoured the Mårbacka folk in every way
on this sojourn. For one thing, they found dear old
friends from Värmland, in whose company they spent
many pleasant hours. They were a Professor Tobiaeson
of Filipstad, his wife and two sisters, and Professor
Lundström, a bachelor—all of their own social circle.

Together, they made up a boating party and went
sailing nearly every day. These outings were the
delight of the children, for the Lieutenant, in his inimitable way, would then tell of his interesting encounters
with the Strömstad folk. Besides, they always had a
couple of large, well-stocked hampers in the boat, so
that when they grew tired of sailing they could go ashore
on one of the little rock islands and have a picnic spread.
Then the children would run about and gather sea-
shells—something they had never seen before. They

wondered at their being allowed to take as many as they wished of these rare treasures, and they loved them as they loved the flowers and the berries of the field.

They were now out on one of their cruises. The weather was fine with just enough wind; the picnic baskets were full of goodies, and the Lieutenant was loaded with anecdotes. Everyone was looking forward to a pleasant evening.

Then, unhappily, some one remarked that they had not yet visited the island just outside Strömstad known as Gray Island. So they immediately decided to lay-to at the island on the return sail, and have their little supper there.

It seems that some hundred years back there lived on Gray Island an infamous old troll named Tita Gray, who was said to be more powerful than the Old Nick himself. When she was alive no human being was allowed to set foot on the island. Those who ventured met with instant mishap—broke an arm or a leg or slipped on the slimy rocks, and fell into the sea.

Since Tita Gray had long been dead and gone, it must be quite safe to visit the island, they thought. All the same the skipper warned them. He told how he and a couple of fellows were walking across the island one day in the spring, when suddenly one of them went down a cleft and fractured his leg.

That made the island all the more alluring to the party; they could hardly wait to set foot on it. Presently the boat turned toward the island and slipped in under the towering cliff wall. The skipper looked for a suitable mooring place.

Just then little Anna pulled at her mother's arm, and said: "Mamma, Selma is crying."

True, the child sat weeping. She had not been at all afraid during the sail—not till that moment. She, like the others, had thought it would be great fun to go ashore on Gray Island; but now that they were right under the rocky cliff, it looked so dark and menacing.

They all asked her why she was crying, but she would not say. She could not tell them she was afraid of a rock. However, she escaped further questioning, for the skipper had at last found a landing-place, and they had something else to think of.

The instant the boat struck, Professor Lundström seized the painter and jumped ashore. Then, as if an invisible hand had dealt him a blow in the chest, he staggered backwards and slipped off the ledge into the sea.

There was great consternation, and cries of alarm went up, but there was no long agony of suspense. With the swiftness of a gull after a fish, the skipper reached over the side of the boat, nabbed the long professor by the coat-collar and drew him up, dripping wet, of course, but quite unhurt.

Naturally, they were all very much shaken by the ghastly sight of a man going down into the perilous deep, and though, luckily, nothing serious had happened, they could not throw off their depression.

Professor Lundström then suggested that the whole party go ashore, and let him take the boat so that he might go back to Strömstad and change his clothes. As it was only a short sail, the boat could return for them whenever they wished.

But they had had enough of Gray Island. No one felt the least desire to step ashore and climb the threatening cliff.

As they sailed back to Strömstad they must have wondered if after all there was not some truth in the old myth about the island. In any case, it was a strange coincidence that the mishap should have occurred just there. They had been to most of the other little islands of the Strömstad skerries, and all had gone well.

"I thought it almost uncanny when the child began to cry," said one of the sisters Tobiaeson. "I knew then that something would happen."

"Now what does Lieutenant Lagerlöf think about it?" queried the other sister.

"What do I think? Well," he replied, "I say it couldn't have turned out differently when we sent a school-priest like him ashore. He was no man for Tita Gray."

"Do you mean, Lieutenant, that if we had sent another—yourself perhaps—we would have had a better reception?"

"Gad, yes!" exploded the Lieutenant.

Lord, how they laughed! The pall of gloom lifted in

a twinkling, as they pictured the meeting between Lieutenant Lagerlöf and Tita Gray.

Aye, aye, he knew right enough that he could have managed her.

Lord, how they laughed!

VII

THE BIRD OF PARADISE

THEY had taken for the summer a cosy little cottage at the end of Karlagatan, where they were so happy and content that Lieutenant Lagerlöf and the children named the place Little Mårbacka, which was assuredly the highest title of distinction they could bestow on a house in a strange city.

The little house fronted a bit of a garden enclosed by a picket-fence, and under the spreading trees they had their breakfasts and suppers. At the back of the house were a couple of potato patches, beyond which, over against a high cliff, stood a tiny hut not much larger than the cabin on the *Uddeholm.*

In that hut lived their hostess, Fru Strömberg, who was the wife of a sea captain. During the winter months she occupied the cottage herself, but summers she always let it to visitors. She now sat in her tiny cabin from morn till night, surrounded by blooming oleanders and tables and shelves laden with curios her husband had brought from foreign parts.

When Fru Lagerlöf and Mamselle Lovisa were having coffee with their friends and the Lieutenant had gone mackerel-fishing, and when Anna had gone over to the candy man's daughters' and Johan to his crabs, Back-Kaisa and Selma would repair to Fru Strömberg's cabin.

Fru Strömberg was their special friend, and to sit with her under the oleanders was as restful as sitting with Grandmother on the corner sofa at Mårbacka. She could not tell stories, but she had many wonderful things to show them: big sea-shells that were full of sound and murmured when you put them to your ear; porcelain men from China with long pig-tails and long moustaches; and she had besides two very big shells, one a cocoanut, the other an ostrich egg.

Back-Kaisa and Fru Strömberg talked mostly of serious and religious things, which the child did not understand; but sometimes they touched on lighter subjects.

Fru Strömberg spoke of her husband and his voyages. He had a fine big ship called the *Jacob*, and just now he was on a voyage to St. Ypes, Portugal, to take on a cargo of salt. Back-Kaisa wondered how Fru Strömberg could have any peace of mind, knowing that her husband was drifting about on the perilous seas; Fru Strömberg replied that there was One who protected him, and therefore she felt that he was as safe on board his ship as when at home in the streets of Strömstad.

The kindly Fru Strömberg then turned to the little girl and said she hoped the captain would soon be at home, for there was something on the *Jacob* she thought

Selma might like to see. They had a bird of paradise there.

"What is that?" asked the child, all interest now.

"It is a bird from Paradise," Fru Strömberg told her.

"Selma has heard her grandmother talk about Paradise," Back-Kaisa put in.

Yes, of course. She remembered that Granny had told her about Paradise, and that she (Selma) had pictured it as a place that looked like the little rose-garden on the west side of the house at Mårbacka. At the same time it was clear to her that Paradise had something to do with God. And now she somehow got the impression that the one who guarded Fru Strömberg's husband so that he was as safe at sea as on land was the bird of paradise.

She wanted so much to meet that bird. It might be able to help her. Everyone felt so sorry for her mamma and papa because she was not getting well. And to think that they had made this expensive trip only on her account.

She would have liked to ask Back-Kaisa and Fru Strömberg whether they thought the bird of paradise would do something for her, but she was too shy. They might laugh at her, she feared. But she did not forget what Fru Strömberg had told her. Every day she wished the *Jacob* would come, so that the bird of paradise could fly ashore.

Then one day she heard, to her great joy, that the *Jacob* had arrived. But she did not speak of this to any one. To her there was something very sacred and mysterious about it all. Remembering how solemn her grandmother had been when telling about Adam and Eve, she did not want to tell Johan and Anna that on the *Jacob* there was a bird from Paradise which she was going to ask to cure her leg. No, she would not speak of it even to Back-Kaisa.

Now every time she went to see Fru Strömberg she expected to find the bird sitting warbling in one of her oleanders. But he did not appear. How strange! she thought. One day she asked Back-Kaisa about it, and was told the bird was on the ship. "But you'll soon see it," said Back-Kaisa, "for to-morrow we're all going on board the *Jacob*."

It seems that Captain Strömberg had hardly been home a day before he and Lieutenant Lagerlöf were bosom friends. The Lieutenant had already been out on the *Jacob* several times, and liked it so well that nothing would do but the whole family must see what a fine ship she was.

When they set out none of them had any real notion as to what boarding the *Jacob* meant. The little girl thought the ship would be lying alongside the quay like the big steamers. But indeed she lay in the offing. They had to get into a little boat and row out. It was strange to see that the nearer they got to the ship the larger she grew, till at last she loomed high as a mountain. To those in the rowboat it looked quite impossible to clamber up *there*.

Mamselle Lovisa said straight out that if it was to that high boat they were rowing she could not go aboard.

"Wait a bit, Lovisa," said the Lieutenant, "and you'll see it's easier than you imagine."

Then Mamselle Lovisa declared she would as soon think of climbing the flagpole at Laholmen. She thought they had better turn back at once.

Fru Lagerlöf and Back-Kaisa agreed with her, and were for going home. But Lieutenant Lagerlöf stuck to his point. There was no fear but they'd get aboard all right, he said. This was perhaps their one chance of a lifetime to see how it looked on a merchant vessel; and they ought not to miss such an opportunity.

"But once we're up we'll never be able to get down again," argued Mamselle Lovisa.

They met a boat laden with sacks.

"See that boat, Lovisa?" the Lieutenant said. "Do you know what's in those sacks?"

"My dear Gustaf," returned Mamselle Lovisa wearily, "how should I know?"

"Well, they're sacks of salt from the *Jacob*," the Lieutenant informed her. "They have neither arms nor legs, yet they've come off the ship; so surely you should be able to do it."

"You ought to dress up once in crinoline and long skirts," snapped Mamselle Lovisa, "then perhaps you'd not be so brave."

They went on like that the whole way out to the ship. The little girl who so longed to meet the bird of paradise wished with all her heart that her father might induce her aunt and the others to go on board; though she, too, thought they could never in the world get up there.

All the same they presently lay-to under a swaying rope-ladder. A couple of sailors jumped into the boat to help them with the climb. The first to be taken was the little sick girl. One of the sailors boosted her to his comrade, who bore her up the ladder and put her down on the deck; here he left her to go and help the others.

She found herself standing quite alone on a narrow strip of deck. Before her opened a great yawning hole, at the bottom of which something white was being put into sacks. She stood there a long while. Some of the folks down in the boat must have raised objections to climbing the ladder, since no one appeared. When the little girl had got her bearings, she glanced about for the bird of paradise. She looked up at the rigging and tackle. She had pictured the bird as being at least as large as a turkey, and easy for the eye to find.

Seeing no sign of it, she turned to the Captain's cabin-boy, who had just come up, and asked him where the bird of paradise was.

"Come along," he said, "and you shall see him." He gave her a hand lest she might fall down the hole; then walking backwards, he led her down the companionway into the Captain's cabin—a fine room, with polished mahogany walls and mahogany furniture.

In there, sure enough, was the bird of paradise!

The bird was even more beautiful than her imagination had pictured it. It was not alive, yet it stood in the middle of the table—whole and perfect in all its gorgeous plumage.

The little girl climbed up on to a chair and from there to the table. Then she sat down beside the bird and regarded its beauty. The cabin-boy, who stood by, showed her its long, light, drooping feathers.

"Look!" he said. "You can see he's from Paradise, for he hasn't any feet."[1]

Now that seemed to fit in very well with her own concept of Paradise: a place where one did not have to walk but moved about on wings. She gazed at the bird in adoration, her hands folded as in prayer. She wondered if the cabin-boy knew it was the bird that protected Captain Strömberg, but dared not ask him.

The child could have sat there all day lost in wonder; but her reverie was suddenly interrupted by loud shouts from the deck. It sounded as if someone were calling, "Selma! Selma!"

Immediately afterwards, they all came rushing into the cabin—Lieutenant Lagerlöf, Back-Kaisa, Fru Lagerlöf, Captain Strömberg, Johan, and Anna. They were so many they quite filled the room.

"How did you get here?" they asked as with one breath—wonder and amazement depicted on their faces.

---

[1] The first birds of paradise seen in Europe were mounted without feet.— TRANSLATOR.

With that, the little girl remembered that she had walked on the deck, had walked down the stairs and into the cabin—that no one had carried her.

"Now come down off the table," said one, "and let us see whether you can walk."

She crawled from the table to the chair, and from the chair to the floor. Yes, she could both stand and walk.

How they rejoiced! Their hopes had not been in vain; the object of the journey was fulfilled. The little girl was not going to grow up a helpless cripple, but a normal human being.

The grown folk said it was the splendid baths at Strömstad that had wrought the change. With tears of joy and gratitude, they blessed the sea, the air, the city and all therein—glad they had come.

The little girl, meanwhile, had her own thoughts about it. She wondered if it was not the bird of paradise that had helped her. Was it not the little marvel with the quivering wings which had come from that land where feet were not needed that had taught her to walk here on this earth, where it was such a very necessary thing?

VIII

THEY had said good-bye to Fru Strömberg and "Little Mårbacka." The children had packed away their precious sea-shells and the grown-ups had locked their trunks. They were now going aboard the steamer that was to bear them away from Strömstad.

A lot of people had gathered at the wharf. There stood Captain Strömberg, their boating companions, and other summer visitors whose acquaintance they had made, and many, many more.

"All the old pilots and skippers and fishermen in town must be here," observed a gentleman who had cruised with the Mårbacka folk.

"Yes; and all the fishwives and female bath attendants to boot," said another.

"They must have come down to bid Gustaf good-bye," Fru Lagerlöf remarked. "He seems to know everyone."

Lieutenant Lagerlöf had to say farewell to so many that he came near losing the boat. They all knew he had come to Strömstad to seek a cure for a little child that could not walk, and had taken this op-

portunity to offer their felicitations on the happy out-
come.

"Ay, but it's good, Lieutenant, to see the little gal
standin' on the deck with the other kiddies," said an
old fisherman.

"It must have been your weakfish, Olaus, that set her
up."

"Ay, weakfish's good eatin'," the old man nodded.

The Lieutenant had already turned to a group of
bath attendants.

"I give you thanks," he said, "for you, also, had a
share in the good work."

"You must come aboard, Gustaf," Fru Lagerlöf
shouted from the deck. "The siren has sounded for
the third time."

At the very last moment two little girls ran up the
gangplank and over to the Lagerlöf girls. They
curtsied, shook hands, wished them *bon voyage*, slipped
Anna and Selma each a parcel, then hurried ashore.

They were the daughters of the confectioner with
whom Anna had played all summer. Selma hardly
knew them at all, and was quite overwhelmed by their
kindness in giving her, too, a parting gift.

Unfolding the wrapper, she found something very
pretty—a strip of bright red satin ribbon, pasted on a
bit of cardboard, on which there were some letters
embroidered in black silk.

"It's a bookmark," Back-Kaisa said; "and that you
should lay in the prayer book."

"'Remembrance' it says there," her mother explained. "That means you must never forget the little girl who worked it for you."

The red satin ribbon with the black embroidered letters nestled between the covers of her prayer book for many, many years. When on a Sunday at church she would open the book and let her eyes rest on the bit of ribbon, it carried her back in memory to days long gone by.

She sensed the odours of the sea and before her eyes rose a vision of boats and sea-faring folk—hardly the sea itself, but sea-shells and jelly-fish and crabs and star-fish and weakfish and mackerel. Then from some obscure recess of memory emerged the little red house in Karlagatan. She saw the bird of paradise, Fru Strömberg, the *Jacob*, Gray Island, Östra Hamngatan, the *Uddeholm*, and the three horses that drew the big carriage. And last, she saw the horses turn in on a large sward, surrounded by low red buildings and enclosed by a white fence. They stopped before a wide red house, with small windows and a little porch, and she heard all in the carriage cry as with one voice: "Thank God we're home again!"

The others, she remembered, recognized the place at once as Mårbacka, but not she. Had she been alone she would not have known what place it was. To be sure, she remembered her home, though until then she had never seen how it looked.

On the porch stood a little sweet-faced, slightly bent, white-haired old lady in a striped skirt and black jacket. That was her grandmother. Her she remembered quite well, though she had never before noticed her appearance.

It was the same with her brother Daniel and the baby, the housekeeper and Othello the spaniel—they were all quite new to her. True, she remembered them in a way; but this was the first time she had actually seen them.

Moreover, sitting in the little church, her head bowed over the prayer book, she knew that on that Strömstad visit she had not only learned to walk but to see.

It was thanks to that journey that she remembered her nearest and dearest as they were in their prime, when life was a joy to them. But for that, everything relating to those times would have faded out of mind. But with the help of the little red ribbon they lived on. "Let not forgetfulness grow over all this," the ribbon said to her. "Remember your parents, who gave themselves no rest till they had found a cure for you. Remember Back-Kaisa, her great love and patience, how she braved the terrors of land and sea for your sake."

THE OLD HOUSEKEEPER'S TALES

I

GRANDMOTHER

THE year after the Strömstad visit the little Mårbacka children had a great sorrow. They lost their dear grandmother.

Almost up to the very last they had sat with her on the corner sofa in the bedroom and listened to her stories and songs. They could not remember a time when their grandmother had not sung and narrated to them. It had been a glorious life. Never were children so favoured.

Where their grandmother had learned her stories and ballads they did not know, but she herself believed every word of them. When she had told something very wonderful, she would look deep into the eyes of the little children and say, with the utmost conviction: "All this is as true as that I see you and you see me."

One morning when the children came down to breakfast they were not allowed to go into the kitchen-bedroom as usual to say good-morning to grandmother, because she was ill. All that day the corner sofa stood empty and it seemed as if the long storyless hours would never end.

A few days later the children were told their grandmother was dead, and when she lay shrouded they were brought in to kiss her hand. But they were afraid. Then some one said it was the last time they might thank Grandmother for all the pleasure she had given them. And then came the day when the stories and songs were borne away, shut up in a long black box, never to come again.

It was a sad loss to the little ones. It seemed as if the door to a beautiful, enchanted world, where they had freely passed in and out, had been closed. Now there was no one who knew how to open that door.

But after a while they learned to play with dolls and toys like other children, and then it may have appeared as if they no longer missed their grandmother or remembered her. But indeed she lived on in their hearts. They never tired of listening to the stories of her the old housekeeper told; they prized them as treasures they wanted to keep always.

THE GHOST OF VILARSTENSBACKEN

THE old housekeeper used to say it could not have been so very long ago that Mårbacka was first laid under the plow and became a regular homestead. In the old mistress's youth it was still within man's memory that the place had been a summer *säter* belonging to one of the old peasant farms to the west of the dale, nearer the Fryken.

But when in the world it was that the first herd of cattle grazed there and the first cattle-sheds were built, who could say? Herdsmen can hold to a place for thousands of years without leaving a trace after them. And indeed there was not much here at Mårbacka that had come down from their time.

The name Mårbacka, the old mistress believed, one of the herdsmen had given to the hilly moors below Åsberget, where they drove their horses and cattle to grass. She also thought they and their animals had beaten the roads.

That the herdsmen had broken the south road, along Åsberget, was clear, because from that direction they would have had to come with their cattle. The steep road to the east, which went straight down the mountain, was probably their work. By that they must have gone when they wished to visit *säter* folk on the other side of the mountain. The wretched road running northwest, toward Sunne, must once have been an old goat-path, and westward they could hardly have had any passage at all. To the west lay swampy bottom-lands, through which ran a tortuous river. When the shepherdess stood upon the flat stone outside her *säter* cabin, she could see her home-farm on the other side of the dale; but to get there, she had to go a long way round, to north or southward.

The herdsmen must have wandered up from the south mostly, for Vilarsten, or Resting-stone, where they were wont to rest after their long tramp, still lay at the roadside, just south of the farm. But there was something about that road that made people afraid to venture out on it after dark.

At the time that Mårbacka was a summer *säter* there lived in the parish of Sunne a priest who was so harsh and exacting that a man who had been a servant in his home a few months went and hanged himself. The priest, when he learned what had happened, with-out stopping to think, cut the body down and carried it out into the yard. Then, because he had touched a suicide, and for no other reason, he was regarded as polluted and disgraced. The people of Sunne would not allow him to set foot in the church, which remained closed until another clergyman was called.

The Sunne priest used also to officiate at Åmtervik,

where they had a church and a little parish house but no resident clergyman. He probably thought that in an out-of-the-way place like Ämtervik no one would know of his being "unclean"; there, surely, he might celebrate the Mass, as usual. So he rode down to Ämtervik. But the evil report was there before him. As he stood at the altar intoning the Mass, murmurs ran through the congregation; the people thought him unworthy to stand in the House of God. Nor did it end there. The Ämtervik peasants felt that he had shown them great disrespect. They were as good men as the Sunne folk, they said, and would not have a priest others had repudiated.

A few among the younger peasants got together and planned to give him something to remember. But knowing it was dangerous to lay violent hands on a priest, they decided to wait till he set out for home. He rode alone, and there were many lonely spots along the bridle-paths between Ämtervik and Sunne where the men could lie in wait for him.

The priest must have sensed danger, for instead of taking the usual road to Sunne to the west of the dale, he took the *säter* paths to eastward past Mårbacka— thinking to find his way home.

The men, ambushed at the roadside, seeing no sign of the priest, knew of course that he had eluded them, and thought they would have to go home without carrying out their purpose. But it happened that one of the men was a brother to the servant who had taken his own life on account of the priest and he was not going to let him escape so easily. He seized a long stackpole which had been left standing in the field since haying time, and set off toward the marshes; the others did likewise—running and leaping across the bogs. Just below Mårbacka-säter they touched firm ground; then, hurrying southward to intercept the priest, they came upon him in the road near the Resting-stone.

It may have been their intention merely to give him a sound thrashing; but, unluckily, there was the man who had a brother to avenge. He had a sword concealed under his cloak, and when the others had pulled the priest off the horse and thrown him to the ground, the man drew his sword and cut off the priest's head.

The moment the deed was done they were filled with terror of discovery, and thought only of escape. They let the horse run loose and left the corpse lying at the roadside, to make it appear that the murder had been committed by wild robbers. Running for home by the way they had come, over the bogs, they hoped no one had seen them. They had not been on any passable road, and their venturing across the marshes would not have aroused suspicion.

Things went better than they expected. Inasmuch as the priest had been at odds with his parishioners, there was no eager search for him. When at last his body was found the crime was attributed to robbers and outlaws. Even in death he was regarded as unclean. No one would touch the body. Since the people deemed him unfit to rest in consecrated ground, they let him lie where he was, merely covering him with sod, over which they built a cairn of large stones to prevent wild beasts digging him out.

But the priest could not find rest in the grave thus prepared for him. On moonlight nights he would appear in the road near the Resting-stone in his long cassock, holding his head between his hands. Horses saw him plainer than humans did, and would shy and rear so that riders were frequently obliged to make a long detour through the wild forest.

So long as there were only cowherds and shepherds at Mårbacka, these ghostly appearances meant very little. It was quite another matter when Mårbacka became a regular farmstead. How to lay the ghost none knew, and year after year folk had to take care not to be out on the road near the Resting-stone along about midnight.

The old mistress, however, had assured the housekeeper that nowadays none need fear the headless priest. A housewife at Mårbacka—a strong-minded, determined woman, who knew a little more than the common run of folk—had laid the ghost.

That farm mistress happened to be out riding late one evening along Vilarstensbacken when—just as she expected—the ghost appeared in the road near the cairn, and made as if to bar her way.

The woman was neither awed nor frightened and her

horse was as calm and fearless as herself. She rode right up to the "spook," and began to admonish it.

"Why can't you stay where you belong!" she said. "You know well enough that no better grave awaits you. So don't imagine you will be allowed to lie in churchyard mould—you who were so corrupt when you died."

This was spoken with firm conviction, for she knew, of course, that he had been a hard man, and really considered him unworthy a decent burial.

"You have no cause to rise out of your grave and demand vengeance," she went on, "for you only got what you deserved."

When she said this, the ghost seemed to grow darker and more distinct; it looked as if ready to fall upon her. Quite undaunted, she addressed it again, determined to put an end to that nuisance.

"If you will lie still in your grave I promise you that my eldest son shall take up your calling, and become a priest. He is a good lad and I know that he will be one of those servants of our Lord who turn people's hearts toward God, and not away from Him."

She had barely uttered the first words, when the ghost began to fade in the moonlight till there was nothing left of it but a faint outline; and before she had finished speaking, even that had vanished.

The Ghost of Vilarstensbacken never appeared again.

That torment luckily ended, there was increasing peace and comfort at Mårbacka. The place became as fine a farm as any in the parish, and the owners thrived and prospered.

All this, the old mistress had said, was undoubtedly true, for some years later, in the beginning of the eighteenth century, a youth from Mårbacka was sent to a theological seminary, where he studied for the ministry and was finally ordained.

He called himself Morell, after his ancestral home, and in due time was made curate at Ämtervik. He settled on his family estate (Mårbacka), and was the first clergyman to reside within the parish—his predecessors having all lived at Sunne and come down to Ämtervik only on specified Sundays.

The peasants of Ämtervik were very glad to have their own pastor, especially one who had a home of his own so that they did not have to provide him with a living. To be sure, Mårbacka was a good distance away from the church, but that disadvantage was more than made up for by the priest's being a man of independent means.

The parson's pay was small, and of that little the lion's share went to the Dean of Sunne, so that the priest would have been as poor as the proverbial church mouse but for Mårbacka.

In order that this arrangement, which was for the good of both pastor and parishioners, might be perpetuated, the first clergyman at Mårbacka gave one of his daughters in marriage to a priest by the name of Lyselius, whom he made his heir to the estate and the office.

Lyselius, in his turn, did likewise: he married one
of his daughters to Pastor Eric Wennervik, who later
came into the property and the office.

The old mistress had said that everyone seemed to
think this an excellent custom which should be kept
up; even the clergymen's daughters, she thought, had
been content to have it so.

III

THE old mistress had also said it was the three clergymen, Morell, Lyselius, and Wennervik, who built up Mårbacka.

Before their time the place was just a peasant farm, which, though large and flourishing, looked like any other farmstead. If there were a barn for ten cows and a stable for two horses, it was about all that could be expected. The main house had perhaps but one large room, where the entire household lived day and night, and a little pitch-dark kitchen called the *kåve*. There were many other buildings, of course—a larder, a bath house, a rye-loft and other sheds, a kiln, and a smithy; but they must have been rather small, as the farm at that time was not nearly so extensive as it is now. Only the nearest fields were then under cultivation.

The old mistress used to wonder how the three clergymen had managed to build a stable for ten horses and a cow-house for thirty cows, besides all the big granaries, storehouses, and sheds which they seemed to have required. The brew house with an adjoining room, which was used for a farm-office, were also from their

time, likewise the milk-room, loom-room, and bailiff's
lodge.

Finally, along in the seventeen-nineties the old mistress's father, Pastor Wennervik, built a new dwelling
which was planned on a more modest scale than the
other buildings. He was satisfied with a one-story
house of four rooms and kitchen, and an attic with two
gable chambers. But all the rooms, including the
kitchen, were large and light, and so admirably adapted
to living purposes that hominess, so to speak, met one
with open arms at the threshold.

Pastor Wennervik had also laid out the kitchen garden with its aromatic herb-beds and fruit trees, and the
little rose garden. He was the son of a master gardener,
and was himself quite clever at gardening. Many
little rose bushes and grafted apple trees still growing
on the farms round Ämtervik he had helped set out.

In his youth he had been tutor at a great manor, where
he conceived a fancy for fences and gates. Round
the kitchen garden at Mårbacka he put a pretty white
paling, with ornamental gates, and another round the
rose garden. If one wished to drive in from the road,
one had first to open a great gate, then pass range on
range of out-buildings, with fences and gates at several
points. It was the same with the front yard.

The children loved to hear about their great-grandfather, Pastor Wennervik. They had found in a corner
cupboard of the farm-office some old books in Greek and
Latin which bore his signature, also a number of poems

by Bellman and Leopold copied in his hand. They knew that the harpsichord and guitar had come to Mårbacka in his time, and they created in fancy a beautiful image of him. It was not only from the old housekeeper they had heard anecdotes of him, but also from their father and their father's sisters. He was a charming gentleman of fine taste, who always liked to wear good clothes and who loved flowers and apples. He must have been a bird-lover, too, for it was he who put up the octangular dove-cote that stood on the green outside the kitchen window. He had planned and worked to make Mårbacka a beautiful home. The clergymen who dwelt there before him must have lived mostly in the peasant manner, while he had softened the old severe simplicity by introducing some of the manners and customs of gentlefolk, thus rendering life there richer and easier.

There was an old oil painting at Mårbacka from the time of Pastor Wennervik. It was a portrait of his early love—a rich and high-born young lady of the Province of Västergötland. He had been tutor to her brother, and being no doubt the best looking and most charming young man she had met up to then, she fell in love with him, and he with her. The lovers had their trysting places in the bowers of the manor park, where they spoke of their love and pledged eternal fidelity. But one day they were discovered, and the young tutor was promptly dismissed.

All that was left to him of love's young dream was this

counterfeit presentment of his sweetheart. The young lady's portrait had not been done by a skilled artist; the face on the canvas under the powdered hair was set and expressionless; it looked more like a pretty doll than the likeness of a human countenance. However, the features were of delicate mould, and to him who had seen her eyes sparkle and her lips curve in a smile, the portrait was beautiful enough. Pastor Wennervik perhaps felt some of the old glow of youth in his heart when his gaze rested on the picture.

Mayhap 'twas the portrait which inspired the obscure country parson to surround himself with flowers and birds, to enhance the beauty of life with music and poetry.

IV

THE GANDER

THERE was only one thing the children had against Pastor Wennervik—that in his late years he had married Jungfru Raklitz, the dreadful old housekeeper-person who had gone from manor to manor and been harassed and tormented by hard mistresses, until she, in her turn, became a plague and a torment.

If Pastor Wennervik must needs have married again he should at least have thought to protect his dear daughter against the stepmother. That she was allowed to treat the girl as she saw fit, to scold and chastise her and put upon her an unreasonable amount of work—that, the children could never forgive him.

How they loved the billy-goat that got drunk on dregs and butted into old Raklitz, upsetting both her and her brandy cruse. They also sided with the market folk at the Ombergshed Fair who stole her apples and shouted back to her that the Mårbacka parson was too good a man to take money from poor folk for his apples. And they gloried in the bold thief who broke into her larder after she'd had a new lock put on the door which was so big and strong it might have done for a prison gate. And they were ready to burst into tears at the thought of the poor goosey-gander!

One fine April day, in the time of Fru Raklitz, all the Mårbacka geese had been let out in the farmyard. Suddenly some wild geese came flying high above them, honking and shrieking as usual. The tame geese flapped their wings and squawked back—the way they do every spring.

As flock after flock of wild geese flew over, the tame geese grew more and more restless, and before any one knew what was up, a big gander darted into the air and joined the wild geese in their flight.

Everyone expected that he would soon turn back; but indeed he did nothing of the sort. When he was not there by the next morning, they thought they'd never lay eyes on him again. He must have fallen prey to the fox or the eagle, they said, if he had not actually become winded and dropped dead from exhaustion. It was inconceivable that a tame goose could fly with wild geese to the far north.

Nothing was seen or heard of the gander the whole summer. But when autumn came, and the wild geese flew southward, shrieking and calling as always, the tame geese again lifted their wings and answered them.

Fru Raklitz, seeing how excited the geese were, and being more wary this time than the last, told her stepdaughter, Lisa Maja, to run out and drive the geese into the barn.

Lisa Maja had no sooner stepped into the barnyard

than she heard a loud rustling noise just over her head, and almost before she had time to blink, a flock of wild geese alighted on the ground right in front of her. A big fine white gander was the leader; behind him walked a gray mother goose, trailed by nine speckled goslings. The girl hardly dared move lest she frighten them away. Very cautiously she opened the barn door and concealed herself behind it.

The goosey-gander made straight for the barn, his family following him. When they were all inside, Lisa Maja stole softly after to see where they had gone. Well, the big goosey-gander had walked right into the goose pen, and was calling and coaxing till those with him went in, too. Then he led them up to the trough, which was full of oats and water, and fell to feeding.

"See, this is what I'm used to," he seemed to be saying to his family. "This is how I have always lived . . . No food worries, only to step up to a full trough."

Lisa Maja quietly slipped out, shutting the door after her, and hurried back to Fru Raklitz.

"Mother dear, do come see!" she said. "The gander who flew away in the spring has come back with a wild goose and nine little goslings."

All her life she regretted having shut in the goosey-gander and told of his return. Fru Raklitz, without saying a word, hunted up the little knife which was used for killing geese, and before sundown the fine white goosey-gander, the nice gray mother goose, and all the pretty goslings were dead and plucked.

"It was a poor reward you gave our goosey-gander, Mother, for coming back to us with so many nice geese," was all she dared say.

"'Twas enough at least to make all the geese on this place understand what happens to those who defy me and try to run away," Fru Raklitz retorted, a malicious smile playing round her hard mouth.

V

THE LEMMINGS

FRU RAKLITZ had been hard enough on Lisa Maja while the father was alive; but when he died, in the year 1801, and she was in full control, she became even more harsh and exacting. The stepdaughter was now wholly at her mercy, without support or protection from any quarter. The girl was but seventeen—too young and inexperienced to hold her own with a canny old woman. She had a brother, to be sure, but he was at Upsala University studying, so that she could not look to him for any help.

The stepmother and she were soon at daggers' points. Fru Raklitz wanted her to marry the clergyman who had succeeded her father, but Lisa Maja would not agree to that. She opposed all the arguments of the stepmother and the parish folk, who thought the old order such an excellent thing. The clergyman's daughter had her own ideas about marriage. She would not marry a man merely because he happened to be the priest at Ämtervik; he must also be the sort she could love.

The new pastor was anxious to put the matter through. He had got into the good graces of the stepmother, who tried to help him by any and every means. As the girl continued to say No, Fru Raklitz one day drove down to Öjervik to see Judge Sandelin, who was Lisa Maja's guardian, and have a talk with him.

It was clear that she would have the support of both the Judge and his wife. They knew Fru Raklitz well; she had been housekeeper at Öjervik for many years and they had always known her to be a wise and prudent woman. Without doubt she was right, they said; the Mårbacka clergyman's daughter should marry the curate. Anything else was out of the question.

Fru Raklitz was invited to stay for supper, and after the meal she and the Judge's wife sat talking till late in the evening. It was eleven o'clock before she finally set off for home. But the sky was clear and there was a moon, so that it looked as if she would have no difficulty.

And now as the chaise moved rapidly along the shore road toward Sunne, Fru Raklitz sat thinking how she would worry and torment the poor stepdaughter in order to break her will. Of course it was only for the girl's own good, she flattered herself so that she need have no conscience in the matter.

Then, all at once, Svarten, the horse, shied with a jerk that nearly upset the chaise. He acted as if he had the staggers; he dashed off the road, across the ditch, and was down in a field before Long-Bengt, the driver, could check him. When the horse was finally under control he was all a-tremble. Without moving from the spot where he stood he lifted his feet, one at a time, then suddenly gave a shriek such as is seldom heard from a horse—and leaped into the air. Back on to the road he would not go. When Long-Bengt tried to urge him on, he reared and came near kicking the chaise to pieces.

"What is it, Bengt, what is it?" gasped Fru Raklitz, clutching the man's arm in her fright. "Has the horse gone mad?"

"That horse has more sense than Frua and me both," answered Long-Bengt. "He's not mad, he sees something we ain't got eyes for to see."

Svarten nosed the ground, snorted, and backed, regardless of the chaise and those in it. Luckily, they were in a field where the summer's rye had been cut, so that the ground was quite smooth and even. They noticed that they were backing toward a broad, deep ditch; but when the vehicle was at the very edge, the horse stopped; he probably thought he had got past the worst danger. Though still nosing the ground and snorting, he made no more leaps.

"You'd better get out, Frua," said Long-Bengt, "while I try to urge him past whatever 'tis he sees."

Fru Raklitz unbuttoned the carriage apron and was about to set foot to the ground, when she drew back with a cry.

"I can't step down, Bengt," she said. . . . "It's moving!"

"I believe Frua's as daft as the horse," laughed Long-Bengt. "What's moving?"

"The ground under us is moving, the whole field is moving." Her voice shook and she felt a lump in her throat.

"*Asch!*" said Long-Bengt, and jumped out. He thought it was a ghost that had frightened the horse. But ghosts were supposed to come out of the air; he had never heard of their creeping along the ground.

And now he wasn't long getting back into the chaise himself, nor did he venture out of it again. What the mistress had said was true—the ground certainly appeared to be moving. It did not tremble as in an earthquake, nor glide away as in a landslide; but it was as if every clod of earth in the field had taken feet and was running toward the lake.

The two in the chaise sat gazing at the ground—and at last they saw what it was that moved: the field was over-run by hordes of little animals; but they were none the less frightened, the two of them. It couldn't be anything real or natural, they thought. Where had they come from—all those creatures? Every spot in the field was alive with them!

The animals—or whatever they were—scurried across the ditch up on to the road and then went rushing down an incline into the lake. Now what sort of creatures could they be, to behave in that way? Had they been of God's creation there would surely have been some end to them; but these kept coming in limitless numbers.

The horse had now become fairly calm. Only when

the little animals ran between his feet he would snort and draw back. Fru Raklitz, meanwhile, was far from calm. Her teeth chattered from fright, and she mumbled and talked to herself. However, she sat still as long as they were in the field. But the horse was not going to stand out there the whole night. He began to move on his own accord; he walked slowly, lifting his feet and putting them down very carefully; but at least he went forward and not backward.

The strange little animals got into the way of the horse and wagon, and there was a grinding, crunching noise as the wheels passed over the tiny bodies.

When Fru Raklitz heard that grinding she jumped to her feet, and began to shriek wildly. Long-Bengt quickly caught her round the waist, to prevent her throwing herself out of the chaise.

"They're after me! They're after me!" she cried. "They're on the wheels—they're on the step—they're in the wagon!"

The horse increased his speed. The chaise moved joltingly as the wheels went over the little animals.

"They're in the chaise, they're in the chaise!" screamed Fru Raklitz, springing up on to the seat. "They're pulling at my skirt—they mean to drag me to the lake!"

Now Long-Bengt had to stand up to hold her back. "By rights, I ought to let you tumble into the road for your meanness," he muttered. All the same he kept his arm round her.

They were at last back on the road and had driven over great swarms of the roving animals, when Svarten suddenly stopped and neighed contentedly.

"It's all over now," said Long-Bengt. "Sit down, Frua."

But Fru Raklitz went on shrieking, "They're in the chaise; they're pulling at my skirt; they'll drag me to the lake." Long-Bengt had to pull her down by main force and set her on the seat. She struggled so hard he dared not let go of her.

"Go on, Svarten!" he said. "You'll have to find the way without me holding the reins."

The horse set off at a trot, while Fru Raklitz, shaking and blubbering, rambled on about their climbing the wheels and trying to get into the chaise.

"You'll have to run, Svarten," said Long-Bengt, "or she'll go clean off her head before we get her home."

Svarten perhaps understood. Anyhow, he must have wanted to get home to his crib, for he took the hills up and down at top speed.

Long-Bengt sat there with beads of cold sweat standing on his forehead; he tried to assure Fru Raklitz that the trouble was over, but she would not believe him.

"You are very kind, Bengt," she whimpered; "but don't tell me we are safe; I hear them, I see them, they are after us, and mean to drive me into the lake."

When they finally stopped before the front porch at Mårbacka and a maid came out to receive her mistress, she was afraid to step down.

"No, no, not you!" she cried. "You have no power, you can't save me from them."

The maid drew back in alarm. She had never heard her mistress speak like that before.

"Go fetch the priest's daughter," said Fru Raklitz—"go fetch Lisa Maja! She is the only one here who has power over the *evil ones*."

"Mamselle Lisa Maja has gone to bed," said the girl.

"Go ask her to come down as quick as she can," Long-Bengt put in. "Tell her Frua got a fright on the way."

Fru Raklitz sat shaking and gibbering until her stepdaughter appeared.

"Ah, God bless you!" cried the woman, holding out her arms to the girl. "Come help me! Don't be angry with me! I'll never be mean to you again."

"What's the matter, Mother dear?" said the girl as she stood by the carriage.

"Come, give me your hand," begged the stepmother. "Dear heart, hold them back while I get down. Don't let them take me! They can't harm you who have power over them."

When she was out of the chaise she fell on the step-daughter's neck, and sobbed: "Don't ever leave me! Don't be angry with me! You shall marry whomever you will, and I'll not say a word."

"She saw something coming home," Long-Bengt explained. "She saw all the little imps of hell let loose, and she thinks they're after her and will drag her into the Fryken."

The priest's daughter put her arm round the stepmother, and said: "Come in, Mother dear! You are at Mårbacka now. Here none of the evil ones can touch you, darling Mother."

Fru Raklitz was so shaken from fright that Lisa Maja had to talk to her as to a little child, to get her to her room and to bed. She would not let her go; so the girl had to sit there holding her hand, and listen to her ravings until daybreak.

From that time forth Fru Raklitz never dared be cruel to her stepdaughter; nor was she ever again her old ruthless self. She kept to her room mostly, and let Lisa Maja run the house. She would lend a hand when there was extra cleaning and furbishing to be done—as before a great holiday or a party—but only in the house, never outside it. Thus she lived until 1835. Whether she had ever any real affection for the stepdaughter is doubtful. But when Lisa Maja was married, and the little ones came, she grew very fond of them. Every day the children would go in to see Granny. She was also very fond of her coffee, and always had a fire going in the tile-stove of her room, so that she could make coffee for herself. She would often treat the children. But their mother thought coffee was not good for little folk, and told them one day they must never drink any of Granny's coffee.

The next day, when the two youngest, Nana and

Lovisa, came out of the grandmother's room, there was a strong odour of coffee about them.

"What did you have at Granny's to-day?" their mother asked them.

"Gruel, Mummie dear," said the two of them as with one mouth.

"What was that gruel made in?" questioned the mother.

"In the coffeepot, Mummie dear," they answered as if they were speaking a piece.

They said it so nicely and they were so little and naïve, that the mother had to laugh in spite of herself.

VI

IN THE southern part of the parish there are tracts where the landscape is more variform and far more beautiful than up north, round Mårbacka. There the Fryken cuts into the land in deep bays—the one after the other—along each of which lie shore-meadows, bordered by leafy woods, and three or four fine old peasant homesteads. Jutting out between the bays are rocky, wood-grown headlands so wild and inhospitable that no one would think of clearing or building there.

One summer's day Lisa Maja Wennervik had ridden down to Bössviken, which is the most southerly bay, to order some of the fine pears ripening there under the protecting hills. The Bössvik folk were very friendly, and she had dropped in at several cottages, so that it was rather late when she left for home.

But the girl was not afraid to ride back alone in the light summer evening. She went slowly, that she might enjoy to the full the beauty of the night; now riding up among the hills through dense woods, where she fancied robbers or bears might spring out at any moment and tear her off her horse; and now down dales of dewy fields, pretty birch groves and light, shimmering streams. There was still a pale rosy glow in the sky, which was reflected in the lake. She had never seen anything lovelier than that night!

All at once she saw a large, beautiful stallion grazing in the shore-meadow of a bay. His coat was a dapple gray, his mane so long it swept the ground, and his tail, which was thick as a rye-sheaf, also reached to the ground. The horse was broad across the hind-quarters and high at the withers; he had a small head, with fine, clear eyes, his legs were slender, his hoofs a silvery white that glistened like polished metal as he lifted them in the grass. His body bore no marks of harness or saddle.

Lisa Maja had just walked her horse, Svarten, down a hillside, and was now going at the same slow pace toward the meadow where the stallion grazed. She went so close to him there was but the fence between them; by putting out her hand she could have stroked his haunches.

The stallion seemed not to have noticed them before; but now he raised his head and looked up at the young girl. And Lisa Maja was so pretty that the young swains would drop axe, or scythe, or whatever they had in hand, when she came riding, and hurry down to the roadside to hang over the fence till she had gone by.

Fancy! When the beautiful stallion raised his eyes to her, there was the same look of admiration in his gaze that the peasant lads sent her from the roadside.

For a moment he stood regarding her, then quickly turned and galloped off—his mane waving in the breeze, his tail standing straight out. Like a streak, he darted across the meadow and down the bay. Near the shore the bay was shallow and shelving, and as he dashed through the shallows the water splashed round him in clouds of foam. Then, all of a sudden, he disappeared.

Lisa Maja thought the horse in his wild flight had gone beyond his depth, and was drowning. She hoped for a second that he would come swimming to the surface again; but no, he did not reappear. And there was not a ripple on the water where he had gone down.

Then Lisa Maja felt a wild desire to ride to the rescue. She could not bear the thought of letting that glorious creature drown without making some effort to save it. With a sharp pull at the bridle, she swung her horse round toward the fence and gave him a dig with her spurs to make him jump it. But Svarten being the kind of horse that knows more than most humans, instead of taking the hurdle, turned and made for home at full gallop. The young girl from her high mount in the side-saddle had not much control over her determined steed; she soon realized that this time it was useless to try to make him obey. Besides, Svarten probably knew what sort of horse it was the girl wished to rescue from the water. By the time Lisa Maja had come to the top of the next hill and found herself in the darkness of a dense pine wood, she, too, knew what it was she had seen.

The silver-gray stallion with the unshodden hoofs and trailing mane she had often heard tell of.   He was none other than the Neckan—the River-god—himself.

When the girl came home to Mårbacka and told the serving-folk of her adventure, they all thought as she did—that she had seen the Neckan and that herself and all on her place had best be careful, or before very long one among them would surely be drowned.

But there is no lake near Mårbacka and the old bottom lands to the west of the estate were by then so well dried out that not a trace of swamp or quagmire remained. Even the river, which had once been broad and treacherous, was now so diminished that in summertime, at least, it was scarcely more than a shallow creek.

However, in the month of August, when the days grew shorter and the mists hovered over river and meadow, it happened that an old man from Mårbacka was walking homeward one evening across the western meadows; what he may have seen or encountered down among the mists no one ever knew—but he did not return that night. The next morning his body was found in the little river, which was so shallow the water scarcely covered him. He had been a crabbed old man and there was perhaps no great mourning for him; but they were all very certain now it was the Neckan Lisa Maja had seen that time; had she followed him into the lake he surely would have drawn her down to his Blue Mansions in the deep.

VII

THE PAYMASTER OF THE REGIMENT

FRU RAKLITZ'S reformation may not have been so complete after all, for the old housekeeper could never sufficiently impress upon the little Lagerlöf children what a fortunate thing it was for Mamselle Lisa Maja that she got so good a husband as Paymaster Daniel Lagerlöf. He was no rich man; but wise, and kindly, and honourable he had always been. In him she had found just the protector she needed.

To be sure he was no priest, but his father and grandfather, his great-grandfather and great-great-grandfather had all been clergymen and married to daughters of clergymen, so that he could claim kinship with all the old clerical families of Värmland. Any preaching or speech-making gift he had not inherited from his forebears, but the tendency to guide and govern a whole community was in his blood. The Ämtervik peasants, who at first thought ill of him because he had married the Mårbacka parson's daughter—thereby upsetting the old order—soon grew accustomed to having him run the important affairs of the parish.

The children were astonished to hear the housekeeper

speak in that way of their grandfather. They had heard stories of him which were common among the people. He was said to have been a great violinist, and in his youth, at least, was so moody and high-strung that the humdrum of home life wore on him and he had to go his own ways.

But that the old housekeeper denied most emphatically. No, indeed, there was nothing queer about the Paymaster of the Regiment. She could not imagine who had put such ideas into the children's heads. It was merely that his official duties forced him to live away on journeys most of the time. As Paymaster of the Regiment once a year he had to travel through the whole of Värmland, to collect the war tax. And not only was he Paymaster of the Regiment, but Manager of the Kymsberg Iron Works, far up by the Norwegian boundary; and all at once he had to be up and off for there. Then, too, he had such a good name that people were always asking him to serve as executor and administrator. Most bothersome of all had been his trusteeship for Judge Sandelin's wife, who had inherited seven foundries from Iron Master Antonsson. He had to spend months on end at these various foundries, straightening out the tangled affairs.

But as soon as ever he could get away he hurried back to Mårbacka. If he chanced to come home some morning, unobserved, he would hunt up his violin and stand outside the bedroom window, and awaken his wife with music.

Now that much may have been true, perhaps; but that he ran away from home and was gone for long periods without letting anyone know his whereabouts—that was just something folks imagined, because 'twas always the wife who ruled at Mårbacka.

The children were very sorry to hear that their grandfather had been such a sober, serious, matter-of-fact person. And of course they had to believe what the old housekeeper told them.

Then, one evening, when their parents had gone to a party, the housemaid, who was to sit up for them, had persuaded Maja, the new nurse, who succeeded Back-Kaisa, to keep her company. They made a fire in the tile-stove of the nursery, drew up the children's little red chairs, and sat talking in whispers so as not to disturb the three little girls, who had gone to bed.

By and by the door creaked and in walked the old housekeeper. She had been wondering where the housemaid had betaken herself, and had been all through the house looking for her. She, too, drew up a chair. Anyway, she declared she'd not be able to sleep till she knew the master and mistress were safely home.

Now that the three of them were seated by the open fire so cosy and intimate-like, the two maids seized the opportunity to ask the old housekeeper's advice in a weighty matter.

"We were just saying, Lina and I, that we ought to

make dream-porridge," said Nurse Maja; "but we
don't know as 'twould do any good."

In that way they tempted the old housekeeper to tell
what had happened when Lisa Maja Wennervik made
a dream-pancake.

On New Year's Eve of the last Christmas Week that
Pastor Wennervik was alive Mamselle Lisa Maja, for
fun, made a dream-pancake. She had just turned
seventeen, and 'twas time for her to be thinking of marriage. So she measured out three spoonfuls of water,
three spoonfuls of meal, and three spoonfuls of salt,
and stirred them together, then she poured the mix-
ture on a hot griddle, ate as much of the pancake as
she could get down, and went right to bed. She must
have had some difficulty getting to sleep, though, for
the salty pancake had given her an awful thirst; and
to drink anything before sleeping would break the
spell.

In the morning she couldn't remember whether
she had dreamt anything. But later in the day, on
going out on the front porch, she stopped in amazement.
All at once she remembered having dreamed in the
night of standing on that very spot. Two strange
men—one old, one young—had come up to her. The
older man had said he was Dean Lagerlöf of Arvika,
and that he had come with his son to ask her if she were
not thirsty and would like a drink of water. With that,
the younger man had immediately stepped forward
and offered her a glass of water. And she was very glad

when she saw the clear, fresh water, for even in her sleep
her throat felt parched.

There the dream ended.   But from that moment she
knew who was to be her husband; for the one who
comes in the dream and offers you water when you have
eaten dream-pancake, he is the one you will marry.

Mamselle Lisa Maja wondered how this could come
about, for at that time she did not know any one by
the name of Lagerlöf.   But one day, soon after New
Year's, as she was standing at the window, a sledge came
up the driveway.   Suddenly she gave a cry and nipped
the housekeeper by the sleeve.

"Here comes the one I saw in the dream," she said.
"You'll find that his name is Lagerlöf."

And 'twas just as she had said.   The man in the sledge
was Daniel Lagerlöf, manager of the Kymsberg Iron
Works, who had come to buy hay.

The first sight of him must have been a disappointment.   He was not handsome and he looked so sombre
she did not see how she could ever like him.

He stayed the night at Mårbacka.   In the morning
the stableboy came in and said that a fox and two
wolves had fallen into the fox-pit.   None of the men
on the place seemed to know what to do to get the
trapped animals out, but the Kymsberg manager jumped
into the pit with no weapon but a knotted stick.   He
dealt the wolves a couple of blows on the head, stunning
them, then slipped a noose round their necks by which
to draw them up

Mamselle Lisa Maja was so taken by the courage of the man, she quite lost her heart to him. She vowed to herself, then and there, that him and none other would she have for a husband.

He, on his part, had fallen in love with her at this their first meeting, though he would not let on. He had once been engaged, it seemed, and although the betrothed was now dead, he felt that he must be true to her memory, and have no thought for another.

At all events, he came to Mårbacka for hay several times that winter. He soon saw that Lisa Maja had none too easy a time of it with that stepmother of hers. He felt sorry for her and wanted to help her. But Lord o' mercy! he couldn't court her himself on account of the dear departed. But there was his brother Elof, who was a priest somewhere up in the Finn-forests; now he might marry her, he thought.

He brought about a meeting between his brother and Lisa Maja—which was the worst thing he could have done. The brother fell desperately in love with the girl, and could think of none but her for the rest of his life; while she loved the Kymsberg manager and had no eyes for his brother.

Pastor Lagerlöf, however, never got so far as to propose. He was commanded by his bishop to marry a person who had lived in his home several years, and to whom he had promised marriage. Fru Raklitz had played a hand in that game, which ended only in misery. For when Pastor Lagerlöf could not have Lisa Maja he took to drink, and finally became as dissolute and worthless as he had once been noble and high-minded.

Now Daniel Lagerlöf had no one to put forward as substitute. If he meant to help the Mårbacka parson's daughter he must come to the scratch himself. Besides, he probably felt now it was better to think of the living than to mourn for the dead. So he actually plucked up courage enough to propose.

Mamselle Lisa Maja was very happy, and thought her troubles would soon be over. But before very long her betrothed began to act strangely, as if he wished to avoid her. He seldom appeared at Mårbacka now, and when he was there he would sit silent for hours and only gaze at her, or he would take out his violin and play from the time he came until he left. At last a whole year went by without her seeing him.

If she asked him when they were to be married he put her off with excuses. Once he said they must wait until he had earned enough to buy out the other heirs to Mårbacka. Another time he had to help put his brothers through college; and again, he thought they had better wait and see whether he'd succeed in getting the post of Paymaster of the Regiment.

He kept postponing and postponing. Now he had too much writing to do, and now too much travelling—till at last no one except Mamselle Lisa Maja herself believed they would ever be married. That made it all the harder for her. Eligible young gentlemen from Sunne—from Ämbervik—now came a-courting. She let them all understand they had their trouble for nothing. But some were so persistent they came again and again, and if she forbade them the house they would lie in wait for her at the edge of the woods, and pop out when she appeared in the road.

All the mean things they could say of Daniel Lagerlöf they took pains to tell her. One time she heard that he consorted with the disreputable, besotten cavaliers who drove about the countryside harrying homesteads, and were the terror of all decent folk; another time she was told that he ran about in the woods like a wild animal. Some chaffed her, saying he had now got the post of Paymaster of the Regiment and could jolly well marry her, unless he'd grown tired of his bargain. Others tried to weaken her by hinting that he was after the daughter of Finn-Eric, who was reputed to be the richest man in the country.

None of that had any effect upon Lisa Maja; she was as happy and confident as ever that it would be as foretold in the dream.

Then one day a rumour reached her ears to the effect that her betrothed had said if he were only released from his engagement he would go abroad, and learn to play the violin properly.

That impressed her as nothing else had. She went down to the stable at once to find Long-Bengt.

She said: "Now, Bengt, you must get out the chaise and drive up to Kymsberg, to fetch the Paymaster of the Regiment; for I wish to speak with him."

"Ay, be sure I'll try, Mamselle," said Long-Bengt. "But what shall I do if he won't come along willingly?"

"Tell him you dare not return without him," she said.

And Long-Bengt went.

It was a day's journey to Kymsberg, and Long-Bengt did not get back until the evening of the second day; but in the chaise with him was the Paymaster of the Regiment.

Mamselle Lisa Maja received him cordially, as usual. She asked him into the living room, and bade him sit down and rest a bit after his long journey. They would hurry with the supper, she said, as he must be hungry.

He paced up and down the room impatiently; he seemed only to be waiting for the moment when he could be off.

When they were seated at table—just they two—Lisa Maja turned to him when the housekeeper came in with the food—as if she'd only been waiting for her—and asked him whether it was true that he wanted to break off with her.

"Oh, yes," he answered, looking solemn as an owl. Such was his wish, of course; she should have guessed that long ago.

The blood rushed to her face. If she had not questioned him about this before, she said, it was because she firmly believed they were destined for each other. Then, with a forced laugh, he asked her what she meant

by that. She flushed crimson. Now she told him in a
few words about the dream-pancake, of how in a dream
she had seen him and his father, and what the father
had said to her.

He put down his knife and fork, and stared in amazement.

"This must be something you have just made up,"
he said.

"You can ask Maja Persdotter if I did not recognize
you and say who you were before you were out of the
sledge, the first time you came to buy hay," said Mamselle Lisa Maja, turning to the housekeeper, who was
then passing round the food.

"But why haven't you spoken of this before?" he
questioned her.

"That, I think, you must understand," she answered.
"I did not wish to hold you by any bond but your
own desire."

For a long moment he sat silent—evidently much
impressed by what he had heard. Presently he asked:

"Can you tell me how the man looked who said he
was Dean Lagerlöf of Arvika?"

"Yes," said she, and went on to describe him. Her
description of the father must have been accurate,
feature for feature, for the son was so startled he in-
voluntarily jumped up from the table.

"But my father died the year I was born," he said.
"You may have heard people speak of him, perhaps?"

"I had never seen a Lagerlöf nor heard of either you or your father before I met you in a dream. Ask Maja Persdotter standing there beside you if she hasn't heard me describe your father many, many times."

He went up close to her. "If only I dared believe this!" He walked round the room and back to her. . . . "Why—then *you* were the one my dear father meant for me, and not——"

What Mamselle Lisa Maja replied the old housekeeper never heard, for she saw 'twas time for her to be going.

The young lovers sat talking together till far into the night, and—well—that autumn they were married.

Mamselle Lisa Maja afterwards told the old housekeeper it was only his morbid conscience that had stood in the way. He had felt he would be wronging the dead sweetheart, and he had brooded over his brother Elof, and thought he had no right to happiness when the brother was so unhappy—and all on account of him.

But in her dream he had found something to hold to, something to be guided by, which gave him the courage to do what he wished above everything.

From the day of his marriage he was a changed man, though during the first years the old despondency came over him at times; but later he was as tranquil and even-tempered as could be. A year after the wedding at Mårbacka his brother was drowned, and then for a while it was pretty hard; but that, too, passed over.

The old mistress and he were married six-and-forty

years, and the last thirty years of their union all was serene; there was no happier couple in the world.

*   *   *

The little children lay in their beds listening and delighting. Until then their grandfather had been to them no more than a wooden image, and now all at once he had come alive.

VIII

THE MILITIA-MEN

IT HAPPENED in the year 1810, when Grandmother Lagerlöf was a young wife and the mother of two little children. She sat one evening by the east window of the kitchen-bedroom; dusk had fallen and 'twas too dark to see to sew. Being well on in March the tallow dips were about used up, so she had taken up her knitting, for her knitting needles she could ply in the deepest darkness.

All at once something made her look out. She could hardly believe her eyes! But a little while before it had been fine clear weather, and now there was a blinding snowstorm. The air was so thick with snow she could barely distinguish the firelight from the window of the manservants' hall directly opposite. The lashing wind swished the snow against the house, and in just the short time she had been sitting there the drifts had piled so high that bushes and fences were buried under them.

Darkness had descended quickly with the coming of the storm, yet she descried several large animals stalking through the drifts toward the farmyard. "I hope the maids will be mindful, and not go out for fire·

wood," she said to herself, "for the *graylegs* are out to-night."

Shortly afterwards she heard a piercing cry and saw a wolf lumber past her window with something in its mouth that struggled and fought. She thought it looked like a child. But whose child could it be? Her own little ones were right beside her, and there were no other children on the farm. Close behind the first wolf came another; it, too, had a child in its gape.

Grandmother couldn't sit still any longer. She jumped up so suddenly she knocked over the chair, and rushed through the kitchen out into the yard. . . . Then she stood stock still. Before her was the calm, beautiful spring evening; not a sign of snow—not a wolf in sight.

She must have fallen asleep over her knitting, she thought, and been dreaming. Yet she felt that back of it all lay something serious.

"We'll have to take precious good care of the little ones," she said to the maids. "That was no dream, it was a warning."

However, the children thrived and waxed fat and rosy. The dream, or vision, or whatever it was, soon passed out of mind, like much else of the same sort.

Along in August a company of poor soldiers came to Mårbacka. The men were ragged, famished, and ill. Their bodies were nothing but skin-and-bone and in their eyes was the look of the ravening wolf. The mark of death was on them all.

They were from Fryksände and other parishes in the northern part of Fryksdalen, they said. But now that they were nearing home they feared their own people would not recognize them. Only two years before they had gone forth as well, strong men. What would the folks at home think of getting them back in such a state they were only fit to be put in the ground. They had not been on the battle field, they had only marched to and fro in cold and hunger. Their fight had been with disease and neglect.

They were many thousand strong when they marched away, but one thousand after another had succumbed. Great numbers had been sent out in open barges on the raging sea in midwinter. How it had gone with those voyagers none knew; but when the boats drifted ashore the crews sat at their oars dead and literally encased in ice. These surviving militia-men, now returning on their own, had often been stoned away from farms and villages on their homeward tramp. What seemed to prey upon them most was that they had not been sent into battle and shot to death, but must still drag on in ceaseless misery. They knew the sort they were—covered with vermin, reeking with filth, and horrible to behold. They did not ask for a bed to lie on or the shelter of a roof; they only begged a few armfuls of straw and a dry mound to rest on.

At Mårbacka the poor soldiers were not greeted with stones. The Paymaster of the Regiment was away, but his wife gave them permission to camp in the backyard, just inside the gates. Huge kettles of porridge and gruel were prepared for the men, and all the clothing that could be spared was turned over to them. The servants continually gathered round their camp to listen to their tales of what they had passed through. Not all could talk, however. Some were too listless to answer when spoken to; they seemed hardly to know who they were or where they were going.

There was great consternation and wonder over these men who had become so changed. Reports of them spread far and wide, and people came long distances to see them.

"That one, they tell me, is the son of Göran Persa," said a stranger who had stood a long while regarding the poor wretches. "But I knew Göran Persa's son; he was a fine lad; there's not a feature the same."

One day a poor widow came wandering to Mårbacka. She was from a little backwoods croft away up north, where, in a perpetual struggle with hunger and want, she managed to sustain life in her body.

"Is there any one among ye by the name of Börje Knutsson?" she inquired, gazing anxiously at the sick yeomen.

No one answered. The men sat on the ground with their legs drawn up, their chins resting on their knees. They would sit like that for hours without moving.

"If there's any one here named Börje Knutsson he must make himself known," said the widow, "for he's my son."

None moved or said a word, none so much as raised his eyes.

"I have wept for the lad every day since he went away," continued the poor woman. "If he's there among ye why doesn't he stand up and say so, for I shouldn't know him again."

Silence.

The woman slowly went her way. To the first person she met afterwards she related her experience.

"I thought until now I'd go out of my mind if my son did not come back," she said, "but now I thank my God that he's not among those skeletons!"

The militia-men rested a week at Mårbacka, and then went on, somewhat strengthened.

But they had left the bloody flux in their wake. Everyone on the place became desperately ill. All recovered save Grandmother's two little children, who were of too tender an age to resist the virulence of the sickness.

When the two children lay in their coffins, Grandmother said to herself: "If I had done like the others, if instead of harbouring those men I had driven them away with stones, my little ones would have been alive now."

But as that thought crossed her mind, she remembered her vision of that evening in the spring wherein the wolves carried off the children. "Our Lord is not to blame," she said. "He forewarned me." The loss of the children was not due to her act of mercy, but rather to her thoughtlessness in not having taken proper precautions to guard them against contagion.

When she realized that after all it was her own fault
the children were gone, her grief was overwhelming.
"I shall never get over it," she said.   "I can never be
the same again."

Her despair was increased by her fears for the husband—how would he take the loss of their children?   He
had not been at home in several months.   The old
despondency had perhaps come over him again, so that
he dared not come home.   Where he was then she did
not know; so could not even send him word of what had
happened.   Anyway, he would surely regard the death
of his children as a visitation from God for his marrying
her, and never come back.   She was not so certain
but he would be right in this.   It were best perhaps
they never met again.

All on the place were much concerned about her.
What to do to help her they did not know.   But
Long-Bengt, who was the oldest of the servitors, was
not afraid to act sometimes on his own responsibility.
He set off for Kymsberg one morning in quest of the
master.   This time he was not two whole days getting
back.   He actually found the Paymaster of the Regiment and stated his errand.   The words were hardly
out of his mouth before the master ordered a fresh
horse put to the chaise.   They drove all night without
a stop, and reached Mårbacka in the morning.

Now the husband was not glum and difficult when he
came.   He took his wife tenderly in his arms, dried her
tears, and spoke loving words of comfort to her.   It

seemed as if then for the first time, when seeing her so crushed and sorrowful, was he able to reveal the full depth of his love.

"And I thought I should lose you, too!" she said.

"I'm not one that grief can drive away," said he. "Did you think I would desert you because of your great compassion?"

In that moment she understood his heart as never before. She knew that in peaceful and happy days she must rely on herself—which she was well able to do; but in sorrow and suffering and times of stress he would always be by her side—her stay and comfort.

OLD HOUSES AND OLD PEOPLE

I

THE STONE HUTS

WHEN Lieutenant Lagerlöf took over Mårbacka the buildings were mostly very old.
Oldest, however, were the manservants' hall
and the sheep-cot, though the storehouse on stilts,
which served as larder, the stable with the loft balcony,
the bath-house, where they used to smoke bacon, and
the kiln, where they malted grain, were no newcomers
into the world.

The servants' hall and sheepfold were built of stones
which had been picked up on the ground—large and
small, round and flat. The walls were two ells in thick-
ness, as if meant to withstand a siege. That style of
building was not of last year or the year before, so that
in the matter of age those two structures would certainly take precedence.

The first permanent residents of Mårbacka must
have come from some village where there were too
many occupants in every cottage and not enough land
under cultivation to yield bread-food for all. They
were no doubt a young couple who wanted to set up a
home, and saw no other way than to fare forth into the
wilds as settlers. With an eye to the good pasturage

below Åsberget, they took possession of the little huts formerly tenanted by the *säter* lasses. But after a time they perhaps felt unsafe, for they had no neighbours within miles of them. Sometimes the bear paid a visit to the cattle-shed and they themselves received calls from rough gangs of charcoal-burners.

Under such circumstances, naturally they would have put up a couple of stone huts—one for themselves and one for their animals. The building for the animals was the larger; it had no windows, only narrow openings with home-forged iron gratings, through which neither lynx nor bear could squeeze. The floor was just hard, trampled earth, but a partition of rough-hewn beams divided the hut into two rooms. Thus, the animals which do not thrive together could be kept apart. Horses and sheep, which are always friends, were on one side; cows and goats on the other.

The stone hut they built for themselves had only one room, but it had a floor of hand-split boards, two windows, a fireplace, and a chimney. Along the wall opposite the windows, the settler had put up a large bed-cupboard to hold four wide beds—two lower and two upper—in each of which three persons could easily lie side by side. Under the windows was a bench, and before it a large deal table. At the far end of the room, opposite the entrance, was the fireplace.

In Lieutenant Lagerlöf's time, this which had once been the main building and was now the manservants' hall, was but little changed. The cubby-beds, the circular open fireplace, and the low, small-paned windows with the iron gratings, were still there; but the long board-bench and table had been replaced by a planing-bench and a chest of tools. There were two small, round, three-legged stools which might well have come down from the time of the first settler, likewise a worn chopping-block that stood on the hearth.

Here lived the stableman and farmboy; here the farm labourers gathered at rest hours to eat and lounge; hither poor belated wayfarers were shown when they came asking for night harbour. Here Bengt, who had been stableman in the time of the Paymaster of the Regiment, stayed on in his old age. He had worked so long on the place that Lieutenant Lagerlöf had recommended him as one worthy the medal for faithful service.

There was another who was to receive this mark of honour—the old housekeeper. She was not nearly so old as Bengt, and was still in active service. She, who was hale and spry, could drive to church in the family carriage and receive her medal at the chancel; while Bengt was confined to his bed that day with the lumbago and pain in the joints. His medal he would get in any case, but it was a grand celebration he would be missing. It had been reported that the Dean of Sunne would come to Ämtervik that Sunday to address the faithful servants, and would himself place the bright silver medal round their necks.

One can understand it was not very pleasant for Bengt to be lying there in pain and torment while the greatest moment life could have held for him passed him by.

Lieutenant Lagerlöf, on arriving at the church, told the Dean why Bengt had not come. Now there was no one the Dean so loved to honour as a faithful servant, one who had been in the same place all his life, and had shared weal and woe with his master and mistress. So, on hearing that Bengt was ill, he said he would drive down to Mårbacka immediately after the service and personally present the medal to Bengt.

The Lieutenant, though pleased, felt a trifle uneasy. He slipped out of the church as soon as he could do so with propriety, and drove home like lightning, so as to be there a little ahead of the Dean.

Bengt was quickly washed and combed and hustled into his Sunday shirt, his bed was spread with clean sheets, and a fancy quilt was substituted for the old sheepskin rug. The floor was swept, the shavings under the planing-bench were carried out, the sooty cobwebs were torn from the ceiling, fresh juniper twigs were strewn over the floor, chopped spruce-fir spread before the door, and a huge bundle of birch and lilac branches was stuck in the fireplace.

The Dean of Sunne at that time was no less a personage than the venerable Anders Fryxell, the distinguished historian and Member of Parliament. Directly he arrived he went in to see Bengt, accompanied by

Lieutenant and Fru Lagerlöf, Mamselle Lovisa, the old housekeeper, and all the servants. They quietly and reverently lined themselves along the walls of the servants' room, expecting, of course, that the Dean would make a little speech in Bengt's honour.

At first all went as it should go. The Dean read some passages from the Scriptures, and Bengt listened—very still and solemn. Then the Dean said:

"You, Bengt, have been one of those good and faithful servants of whom our Lord speaks."

"Ay," says Bengt from his bed, "that's what I've been."

"You have never considered your own welfare before that of your employer. You have always been mindful of the duties entrusted to you."

"Ay, 'tis all so true," says Bengt. "Many thanks to you, Dean, for those words."

It looked as if these constant interruptions would prove annoying to the Dean, who was a great man, accustomed to the society of grand folk. His was such an impressive personality that one easily became embarrassed in his presence. He was always supreme and always had the last word.

There had been no time for the Dean to prepare a speech, and the address he delivered at the church was hardly suitable for the servants' hall. He cleared his throat once or twice, and began again.

"Bengt, you have been a good and faithful servant."

"Indeed I have," said Bengt.

The blood mounted to the brow of the great and brilliant Dean Fryxell.

"You must be silent, Bengt, when I am speaking," he said.

"Ay, ay," the old man replied. "Sure, I'm not contradicting you, Dean. 'Tis all so true what you're saying."

The Dean got redder and redder. Again he cleared his throat and made a fresh attempt.

"You, Bengt, have been a good and faithful servant, but you have also had good masters."

The old man was so elated at this he simply could not keep still.

"You're right, dear Dean, you're right! They've been grand men, all o' them—Wennervik and the Paymaster of the Regiment and this here Eric Gustaf." He reached over and put his hand on the Lieutenant's shoulder, then stroked him down the arm, his old face ashine with happiness.

Once more the Dean lifted up his voice.

"You must be silent, Bengt, when I'm speaking!"

"Why, of course," said the old man. "But 'tis so right and true every blessed word you've spoken, Dean."

Now the Dean had to smile. "You're irrepressible, Bengt. You will not have to listen to any speech. Here is your medal. May you wear it with health and honour for many years to come."

So saying, the Dean went up to the bedside and

laid the medal on the bosom of the old man's Sunday shirt.

Later, at dinner, the Dean seemed a bit abstracted. "This is the first time in my life I have ever lost myself," he confessed, "but in this world one must have all sorts of experiences."

II

BENGT, for his part, was perfectly satisfied with the Dean's speech. Those words about his having been a good and faithful servant, the medal, the august presence of His Reverence in the servants' hall, and the whole demonstration in his honour, had had the salutary effect of dispelling the ache in his joints and the shooting pains in his back. In the afternoon the old man sat up in bed and related, again and again, to all who would listen, how he had once rescued the money-chest for the Paymaster of the Regiment.

It happened one winter when he and the master were out tax-gathering. They had covered all the eastern districts, and before starting on the western, the Paymaster wanted to go home for a while, as he longed for a sight of his wife and little ones. But that of course he did not mention to Bengt. His excuse was that the horse must be rested a couple of days and the food-box, being empty, needed replenishing. Besides, the money-chest was now so full he thought they'd best drive no further until it had been emptied and the money sent on to Karlstad.

The day they turned their noses toward home there was a big blizzard. The roads were so deep with snow they had to drive at a snail's pace. When they were crossing Klarälven on the ice it was already dusk. Shortly afterward, on coming to Nordsjö Manor, the Paymaster spoke of turning in there to ask for a night's shelter. However, he was anxious to get home, and as they were then within thirteen miles of Mårbacka, he and Bengt decided to drive on. Even though it meant being out in the sledge until ten or eleven at night, sleeping in one's own bed was best.

Coming into the dense forest between Nordsjö and Sandviken, they found the road impassable. The sledge went so heavily the horse had to stop at every step, and neither urging nor coaxing could put life into him.

"This is provoking, Bengt," said the Paymaster. "But isn't there a little forest croft somewhere hereabout?"

"Ay, a bit further on is a hut," Bengt replied; "but you can't take in there, Master!"

"I know what you're thinking of, Bengt. That tavern is said to be the haunt of ruffians and vagabonds, decent folk usually fight shy of it. But what else can we do? We've been three hours getting from Nordsjö here, and the horse is spent. We must get him under cover, where he can rest for the night."

"Well, Master, you do as you think best," said Bengt. When his man spoke in that manner, the Paymaster knew he had his own good reasons for not wishing to put up at that place. So he decided to make another attempt to go on.

The two then got out of the sledge and began to clear a path for the horse, which slowly followed them. It was a heavy task. Bengt worked hard and his master, who had on great boots that went above his knees, a heavy wolfskin coat and thick muffler, was soon all out of breath.

"No, Bengt, my boy, this won't do," said he when they were almost at the forest hut. "Now I'm as used up as the horse is. You'd better go in and ask for house-room.

There was nothing for Bengt to do but obey, though he thought to himself they might better remain out in the sledge all night than betake themselves, with the Crown's money, into that robbers' den. It was plain that this would lead to trouble.

In the hut he found a man and wife sitting quietly by the fire. It cannot be said that they were especially pleased to receive the travellers. They made all sorts of excuses: the guest chamber was cold and they had no bed or bedclothes suitable for a gentleman. All the same they were persuaded. The woman brought in wood and made up a fire in the bedroom, the man took a spade and helped Bengt clear away the snow, so that the horse and sledge could be taken to the shed. When Bengt went back to the sledge he found his master sitting there, sound asleep.

"That one doesn't guard the Crown's money any too well, eh?" grinned the crofter.

"Well, so far he's never lost so much as a shilling of what's the Crown's," Bengt snapped.

Always, when they put up anywhere, the Paymaster would carry in the money-chest and Bengt would follow with the food-box. But now, seeing how tired his master was, Bengt said, as the sledge stood before the wretched shed where the horse was to be stabled:

"Go in to bed, Master, and I'll be along later with the boxes."

"You need only bring in the one," the Paymaster told him.

When Bengt had unharnessed the horse and led it into the shed, he found that his master had already gone inside, and the crofter, too, had disappeared. The strong-box was not in the sledge, and he assumed that the master had taken it in as usual.

The Paymaster of the Regiment sat by the fire in a wretched little room when Bengt came in. He heard him put a box down, but was too dead tired even to turn his head.

"Lock the door, Bengt," he said, "and take out the key."

"'Twas not much use bringing in the empty food-box," Bengt observed.

"That's what I thought," said his master. "But we'll be able to sleep to-night without any supper."

Then he stretched himself out on a bare bench—

great boots, fur coat, and all—slipped a couple of sticks
of wood under his head, and was asleep in a second.
He never slept later than four or five in the morning,
but this time he awoke about two o'clock, quite rested
and refreshed.

"Up, Bengt!" he called. "For God's sake let's be
off at once, so that we can breakfast at Mårbacka."

There was neither lamp nor candle in the room; but
the night was not pitch-dark, and they could see well
enough to grope their way out.

"You take the box, Bengt, and hitch up," said the
Paymaster, "while I go in and settle for the lodging."

In a few moments they drove away. The storm
had abated, and though the road was still heavy with
snow, they made fair progress, now that the horse was
rested.

"After all, it wasn't such a bad idea our stopping
there over night," the Paymaster remarked.

"It turned out better than I expected," said Bengt.
"But I had such bad dreams all night, and thought I
heard a lot of noise. It sounded as if they were pound-
ing and hammering in the crofter's room. I don't
know yet whether they were up working or whether I
was just dreaming."

"No doubt you dreamt they stole my money-chest,"
laughed the Paymaster.

"But, Master—where have you put the box?" the
servant burst out, beginning to fumble about under
the seat.

"The box? . . . Why, you brought that out."

"I?—I carried out the food-box."

"But I told you last evening to bring in only the strong-box, and leave the other."

It must have been a terrible moment for Paymaster Lagerlöf when he realized that through a misunderstanding on the part of his man the money-chest had been left out in the sledge. That the crofter had stolen it was plain. But what had he done with it? Could he have opened it? The chest was the regulation bailiff's strong-box, iron bound, with combination lock. But at that, they might perhaps have pried it open.

They left the horse standing in the road, and ran back to the hut. When they burst into the house they found four rough-looking men sitting by the fire with the crofter and his wife, none of whom showed the least surprise. Bengt knew the men at once for the worst desperadoes in the district.

"Now 'tis just as I said," the woman began, "that ye'd not be able to get home till the snow-plow'd been run afore ye."

"Oh, we'll manage to get home," said the Paymaster of the Regiment. "But my money-chest is still in your house, and that I must have along with me."

"Well, well, can it be possible that ye went off and left the money-box!" said the woman. "Then it must be standing in the bedroom. No one's been in there since ye left."

"The box was not forgotten," said the Paymaster,

sternly. "So produce it at once! You know what happens to those who steal the Crown's money."

"Now where could we hide a big money-chest?" the woman protested blandly. "Ye can see for yerself what's here, and ye're welcome to search the house."

And that Bengt had already done. He had peered and poked into every nook and corner—and had found nothing.

"If you won't give it up willingly," said the Paymaster, "I shall have to leave my man here on guard while I go for the bailiff."

"What, that fellow stay and keep guard over us!" almost laughed the woman.

Nor was it likely that Bengt, single-handed, could have kept six persons quietly seated in the hut while his master went in search of the bailiff. But all this time Bengt had been puzzling over something. He heard a crackling noise coming from the bake-oven, but saw no evidences of dough having been prepared. Without a word, he stole up and flung open the oven door.

"Come here, Master," he cried, "and see the kind of bread they bake in this here oven."

In there on a pyre of burning wood stood the money-chest.

The crofter and his wife now sprang at Bengt, but Paymaster Lagerlöf, who was a powerful man, pushed them back. When the other four, who had also begun to bestir themselves, saw the kind of thrusts he could give, they kept out of his reach. Bengt seized the oven rake and quickly pulled the box down onto the hearth. In his eagerness to find out whether the box had been much damaged, he nearly burned his fingers off.

"Ha! it hasn't been opened," he cried exultantly.

Though the box showed that the thieves had been filing and hammering at it, the good oaken chest was intact; neither lock nor mountings had given way. As a last resort they had put it on the fire. But, luckily, Bengt had been too quick for them—only a bit of one corner was charred.

III

THE LARDER ON STILTS

ALL who had been long on the place thought the building next in age to the stone huts was the old larder that stood on posts. It had not been built by the first settler, but was erected some hundred years after his time, when Mårbacka had become a regular farmstead.

The peasants then living there had hurriedly put up a post-larder, it being the rule that every farm of any pretension must have one. It was a crude structure. The door was so low one had to stoop to enter; but the lock and key were conspicuously large and strong. There were no windows, only small openings, with trap-shutters. In summer there were fly-screens at the openings made of woven splints, through which very little light could penetrate.

The larder had two stories. The upper story being better finished than the lower, it was probably there the peasants stored their valuables.

In Lieutenant Lagerlöf's time the building was as in olden days. It may have had a new roof, perhaps, but the steps were never changed. They were so nar-

row and close together one could scarcely get a foot-
hold. Nor was there ever a pane of glass in the old
building.

In the autumn the larder was something to behold.
On the lower floor there were great bins of newly milled
flour, next which stood two huge vats packed to the
brim with beef and pork in brine, then came cowls and
buckets of beef sausage, pork sausage, and potato sausage
—in fact, all sorts of things that had been made up
during the autumn slaughter. In one corner stood a
barrel of salted herring, a keg of salted whitefish and one
of *sickling*, and generally a firkin of salmon. Besides,
there were tins of salted beans, salted spinach, and
firkins of green and yellow peas.

On the upper floor there were tubs of butter of the
summer's churning stored for winter use. Long rows
of cheeses were arranged on shelves above the openings,
and from the ceiling hung year-old hams. The home-
raised hops were preserved in a sack the size of a bolster,
and the malted grain in a similar one. Here were
provisions for a whole year.

It was the housekeeper who ruled over the larder.
That was her domain, and the key to it seldom got into
another's hands. Mamselle Lovisa might potter in
the pantry or milk-room, but she would hardly have
ventured into the larder. The housekeeper was also
supreme in the kitchen. Making small cakes or putting
up preserves and fruit juices might well be left to Mamselle Lovisa, but when it came to roasting a fowl,

making a cheese, or baking *knäckebröd*, it was the old housekeeper who took charge.

The little Lagerlöf children were very fond of her, and looked up to her as the most important member of the household. They had noticed that whenever relatives came to visit, the first thing they did was to go out to the kitchen and pay their respects to the housekeeper. If anything unusual happened in the family Lieutenant Lagerlöf would always call her in and tell her about it, and when Daniel and Johan were returning to school after the Christmas and summer holidays, they were told to say good-bye to the housekeeper. They had also heard outsiders say that Fru Lagerlöf was in great luck to have such a treasure in her kitchen, that nothing was ever wasted under her watchful eye. They said, moreover, that nowhere else could one get such Christmas ale, such *knäckebröd*, and such tasty dishes as were set before you at Mårbacka. And it was all due to the old housekeeper, they declared. So it was not strange the children regarded her as the main prop of the home, and firmly believed that were she not there Mårbacka would collapse.

Then, one day, little Anna found out a great secret, which gave her an awful fright, and she confided it to her sister Selma. She had overheard two of the maids talking about the housekeeper; they had said she was married and had a husband.

The distress of the two little girls was indescribable. If the housekeeper were actually married and had a husband they could not be sure of keeping her at Mår-backa. What would their mother do without her? And what would they themselves do who got such nice titbits from her whenever they went into the kitchen? And what would happen to the whole place, they wondered?

It was most imperative, therefore, that they should know how the matter stood; so they asked Nurse Maja if it were true that the housekeeper was married and had a husband.

Oh, yes. Nurse Maja knew the whole story. She had heard it from her mother, who was in service at Mårbacka at the time it all happened.

"It is the truth and no lie," said she. The house-keeper's husband was living in Karlstad, and was a boss carpenter. There was no such luck as his being dead!

And this was how it came about: When Lieutenant Lagerlöf and his brother as lads attended school at Karlstad, their mother, the old mistress, had sent her trusted housekeeper along with the boys, to look after them and prepare their meals. While there, she had made the acquaintance of a carpenter, who proposed to her. When on her return to Mårbacka in the spring she announced that she was going to be married, the old mistress was both sad and alarmed at the thought of losing her "greatest treasure."

"And what sort of fellow are you marrying?" she had asked her. "Do you know whether he is a good man?"

Oh, yes, she was certain of that. He was a boss carpenter, who had his own shop and his own home. The house was in order, so that she might be married at once, and she could never have found a better husband.

"But how can you be content to live the year round in a barren city street—you who have always lived in the country?" the old mistress had then said.

Oh, she had no fears as to that. All would be well for her hereafter. She was to have an easy life—no baking, no brewing; she had only to go to the market and bring home whatever was needed.

When the old mistress heard her housekeeper speak in that manner she knew the woman was bent on marriage, and there was nothing to be done but give her a wedding at Mårbacka.

The bridegroom appeared to be a clever, sensible sort, and the day after the wedding he took his bride to Karlstad.

One evening a fortnight later—no, it was hardly that long—as the old mistress went out to the larder to slice some ham for supper (she could never take up the key to the larder but she thought of Maja Persdotter and wondered how she was getting along), she said to herself: "If I had not sent her to Karlstad she would never have met that carpenter and I should still have my good helper, and wouldn't have to run out to the larder twenty times a day, as I do now." Suddenly she saw a figure coming through the birch grove that was the living image of her housekeeper. The nearer the figure approached the more certain was Grandmother Lagerlöf of what she beheld. When Maja Persdotter presently stood before her and said, "Good-evening, Frua," she had to believe her eyes and ears.

"Well, well, is it you, Maja Persdotter!" she exclaimed. "But what brings you here? Haven't you got a good husband?"

"All he does is drink," declared the housekeeper. "He's been drunk every day since the wedding. It's the pure alcohol he should be using in his work he guzzles. I can't put up any longer with such a swine."

"But I thought you were to go to the market and buy all your provisions, in order to escape hard work?"

"I'll work my fingers to the bone for Frua and the children if you'll only take me back!" vowed the housekeeper. "I've wished myself back at Mårbacka day and night since I went away."

"Come in, then, and we'll talk this over with the Paymaster of the Regiment," the old mistress said with tears of joy in her eyes. "God willing, we'll never part again so long as we live," she added.

Nor did they. The housekeeper's husband probably knew it would be useless for him to try to get her back. At all events, he never came to fetch her. The wedding ring she removed from her finger and laid away in her trunk. Nothing more was said about that episode in her life.

Lieutenant Lagerlöf's little daughters should have felt

quite easy in their minds on hearing this; but for a long time afterward they were troubled. Since that carpenter was still alive he might come some day and take her away. Whenever they looked down the road they expected to see him coming. Nurse Maja had told them that if he came and demanded the return of his wife, she would have to go with him.

They did not know just how old the housekeeper was. She herself had forgotten the year of her birth, and the date set down in the parish register was said not to be authentic. She must have been over seventy; but for all that, the carpenter might want her back—fine, capable woman that she was.

Then what would happen to Mårbacka!

THE MANSERVANTS' COTTAGE

IN OLDEN times, when the master had to furnish the clothing for all the servants on his place, the womenfolk must have had their hands full of work the year round. Through the long, dark winter mornings and the long, dark winter evenings, they sat at the spinning wheels drawing out the threads for warp and weft. But the weaving itself was not begun until the spring, when the days grew longer; for such work cannot be done in semi-darkness.

In order to get the coarse wadmal and fine woollen cloth, the linen and cotton webs finished by summer, when the parish tailor came, they had to put speed into the looms. But if a loom stood in the kitchen the work did not go very fast. The weavers should have a place to themselves, where they can work without interruptions. Therefore, in former days every well-conducted farmstead had its special loom-room, and, of course, Mårbacka had one also. This was from the time of the clergymen. They had added a story to the manservants' cottage consisting of two rooms, with clay-coated walls and boarded ceilings; and in each was a tile-stove. The back room was occupied by the farm overseer; and in the front room stood two looms, one at either window.

The loom-room was in use even in Lieutenant Lagerlöf's time, though it was then no longer the custom to pay one's serving-folk their earnings in clothing but in money. It was Fru Lagerlöf's great delight to sit at a loom weaving towelling, bed linen, table linen, floor mats, curtains, furniture coverings, and dress fabrics— in fact, everything of that sort needed in the home. All summer long she had her looms going.

In the autumn, however, the looms were taken out to make room for a long, low table which was well smeared with bezum, and the round, three-legged stools were brought up from the servants' room. That meant that Soldier Svens, the parish shoemaker, was expected. Soon he and his apprentices came shouldering great knapsacks packed full of awls, hammers, bundles of lasts, wax-ends, eyelets, heel-irons and shoe-pegs, all of which were dumped upon the table.

The cobbler was a tall, gaunt man with a shock of black hair and a full black beard. Seeing him for the first time one thought him a fierce and dangerous fellow, more fit for fighting than for the shoemaker's bench. But when he spoke, it was in a soft, timorous voice. His eyes were rather small and mild-looking, and his whole bearing was a bit uncertain. He was perhaps not so very dangerous after all.

Lieutenant Lagerlöf's little children were in high glee when the shoemaker arrived. They bounded up the difficult stairs to the loom-room many times a day. It was not so much for chatter they came—for Soldier Svens was a reticent and diligent man—as to watch the work, to see how a shoe was made, from the stretching of the leather on the last to the cutting out of the bootlaces.

The shoemaker, who usually sat with drooping head, brightened when he heard Lieutenant Lagerlöf's footstep on the stairs. He and the Lieutenant were old regiment comrades. After they had discussed brogans, sole-leather, and boot-grease a while, they fell to reminiscing about Trossnäs Field, and when they were well warmed up to it, the Lieutenant would coax the shoemaker to sing an old war song which was unlike any other battle hymn in that it began thus: *We heroes from Sweden, we do not love to fight.* That song the soldiers had made up when they marched down to Denmark in the year 1848 on the expedition known as the "Sandwich War."

Singularly enough, Shoemaker Svens loved to talk about Tailor Lager, who had sat many a time in that very room in the days of the Paymaster of the Regiment, and who was as merry and full of fun as he was grave and mournful.

"You have probably heard, Lieutenant, how the tailor came to be called Lager," the shoemaker began.

The Lieutenant knew the story as well as he knew his "Our Father," but all the same he replied:

"I may have heard it, Svens, but you tell it—in your way."

"Well, you see, Lager he was a soldier like myself, though he was before my time. They say in the regiment that at first he was called Lars Andersson. Then came orders for the privates to change their names because there were too many Anderssons and Johanssons in the regiment.

"One day at a rally at Trossnäs, the soldiers were called in by your father to say by what name they wished to be known, and to have it set down in the roll.

"Of course Lars Andersson was among them. The Paymaster of the Regiment knew him from of old as a joke-maker, for year after year Lars had sat here at Mårbacka weeks at a stretch, making clothes for the Paymaster and all his folks. From the time he came till he went it was nothing but fun and laughter. He could mimic everybody in the parish and make things disappear like a magician at the fair, and he played on a stick till you thought you heard the whole regiment marching. But he was a bit dangerous, was Lars, for he made up yarns about folk that caused bad feeling among the neighbours.

"'Well, what shall you call yourself, Lars Andersson?' the Paymaster asked him, putting on a stern face so that Lars would not dare come with any of his monkey tricks."

"'Lord preserve the Paymaster of the Regiment!' says he. 'May I call myself anything I like?' He puckered his forehead as if he were trying hard to think of a name.

"'You may, Lars Andersson.' The Paymaster, knowing his man, added, 'But it must be a proper and honourable name, and nothing clownish.'

"You remember, Lieutenant, how your father looked. He was a kind man, but just the sight of him put fear into many a one, for he was a big tall man with bushy black eyebrows.

"But the tailor was not afraid—not he! 'Then,' says he, 'I'll call myself Lagerlöf, for that is both an honourable and respected name. I know of no other in all Värmland that sounds so sweet.'

"The Paymaster of the Regiment must have got hot in the head when he heard that that buffoon wanted to call himself Lagerlöf.

"'No, that won't do,' he said. 'We can't have two with the same name in the regiment.'

"'But,' says the tailor, 'there are at least three Ugglas and four Lilliehööks, and it isn't likely anyone would mistake me for the Paymaster.'

"'No. But can't you see, Lars Andersson, that it would never do,' protested the Paymaster.

"'I wouldn't have chosen that name if you hadn't given me leave to call myself whatever I wished.' The tailor made himself appear very humble and serious. 'I know that when the Paymaster of the Regiment gives you his word you can usually go by it.'

"Then there was a long silence. Paymaster Lagerlöf sat studying how he'd get round this. Aside from the fact that it would make him the butt of the regiment, he didn't care to have a mountebank like that tailor knocking about under the name of Lagerlöf.

"'Look here, Lars,' he finally said, 'it might do well enough here in the regiment for us two to bear the same name, but home at Mårbacka it would never go. So understand, if you insist on this thing you can't do any more tailoring there.'

"That must have given the tailor a scare, for the weeks he sat sewing at Mårbacka were to him the best in the whole year. At no other place did he fare so well, and nowhere else did they laugh so heartily at his yarns and pranks.

"'Perhaps you'd be satisfied to call yourself Lager?' the Paymaster suggested, seeing the fellow was wavering. The tailor must have agreed to that, for he went by the name of Lager the rest of his life."

V

THE "JUNGFRU"

SHE was an old *jungfru* who had once been in
service in the home of Fru Lagerlöf's parents,
at Filipstad, but lived now, in her old age, at
Ämtervik. She had known Fru Lagerlöf as a child,
and used to come to Mårbacka two or three times a
year to see the folks.

The *jungfru* was a tall, good-looking woman with
white hair. She had a strong nose, a firm mouth, and
a grave manner. She liked preachers and missionaries,
and ran to prayer-meetings and sewing-circles. One
could not talk with her about dancing, or novels, or
love affairs; such things were to her an abomination.
Nor did one dare speak ill of any one in her presence,
or even discuss pretty clothes, and she would not hear
about the sinful things that went on in the world.

It was not easy to know just what one should talk
about. Outside of cookery and the weather there
were few topics of conversation one might safely touch
upon. These, to be sure, held out a long while,
but even they could become exhausted, for the *jungfru*
was a person of few words, and her answers were short
and well posed.

There was a way, however, to loosen the *jungfru's* tongue; but it had its drawbacks. She had once on a time been cook at a large deanery. The dean had twenty children, all living and arrived at maturity. That family she continually kept in mind, and her supreme delight was to talk about those people.

The family at Mårbacka were having their usual afternoon coffee in the living room. The coffeepot and tray stood on the big table. Everyone, in turn, went up and poured himself a cup. None took more than one lump of sugar, one wheaten rusk and one of rye, one ring-biscuit, one ginger cookie, and a bit of fresh cake, if there happened to be any. Whereupon each sat down in his accustomed place. Fru Lagerlöf occupied one corner of the sofa, Mamselle Lovisa the other. The Lieutenant always had the rocker, which was his favourite seat. No one else would have ventured to appropriate that. Herr Tyberg, Johan's tutor, took a cane-bottomed chair, and between these four stood a table made from the root of an alder. At one of the little window-tables sat Johan, at the other Anna, while over in the chimney corner, by the folded card table, sat the two little tots, Selma and Gerda; they were considered too young to have coffee, and had to be content with a glass of milk each.

The *jungfru*, who had come that day for a visit, was having coffee with the family. She had placed her chair in the middle of the room, where all might see and talk with her. They had run the whole gamut of harmless

"Tell us, what was it?" Herr Tyberg struck in.

Again came a titter from the chimney-corner. The *jungfru* shot the children and Herr Tyberg each a glance that scared them into silence.

"The third was a boy called Noah. And d'you know, *Frua*, he was so good at fishing, and brought home such big catches that both me and his mother was thankful to him. He became a priest in Halland, and every year he sent his folks a big barrel of salted salmon."

"Oh, speaking of salmon——" The Lieutenant started to say something about their ordering another firkin of salmon, but couldn't get a word in for the *jungfru*.

"The next was a boy named Shem," she rattled on. "He was as great a hunter as Noah was a fisher. Oh, you'd ought t've seen all the grouse and hares he brought home! And he became a priest, too, and got a vicarage down in Skåne; and every winter he sent home a reindeer he'd shot himself."

After Shem she took breath and looked round. Her hearers sat silent and subdued. None thought of interrupting her.

"The one that came after the three boys was a girl whose name was Sara. And I'd be willing to swear before God and man, that never have I seen any one with such a knack at putting up pickles and making jam and fruit juice. All the same, she didn't get married; she went to Stockholm and kept house for her brother the Court Chaplain.

"The next was also a girl, and Rebecca was her name. I must say that she was the one who understood me the least. She had such a good head for learning she could have been a priest like her brothers. And the way she could make up poetry was something wonderful! Folks said there was nobody in all Sweden beat her writing cradle songs. Just the same she got married, but 'twas only to a school teacher."

At that point the *jungfru* was interrupted by the maid coming in with fresh coffee, and they must all have a second cup.

"I wonder if there was any one in that batch who could make a decent cup of coffee?" Lieutenant Lagerlöf ventured.

"The Lieutenant takes the words out of my mouth!" exclaimed the *jungfru*. "It may sound queer, but the one who had a real turn for cooking was the fourth boy, Isaac. He was so clever at whipping up a sauce and basting a roast that one could have right good help from him round the stove."

"He must have excelled, though, at preparing baby-food," Herr Tyberg observed.

Snickers went up not only from the chimney-corner, but from all parts of the room. Fru Lagerlöf, however, kept a straight face.

"What a wonderful memory Jungfru Anna must have to be able to remember all that!" she said, so as to keep the old girl in good humour.

Ordinarily the *jungfru* was quick to take offence, but

not when she could talk about her dear deanery children. Then she was imperturbable. At all events, Herr Tyberg had helped them away from Isaac. They never learned to what uses he eventually put his talent.

"The two next were twins, and they were called Jacob and Esau. They were as like as two coffee beans. I couldn't tell one from t'other. I never saw such boys for running and jumping and skating. But they became priests, they, too."

"I thought they were going to be rope-dancers," the Lieutenant cut in.

"They became priests, they, too," the *jungfru* reiterated, not in the least put out. "Esau went up to Jämtland, where he had to clamber 'mong the fells, and Jacob, he went down to Bohuslän, where he scrambled in and out of boats and ships. They found their right places and turned to use the talents God had given 'em—they, like their brothers and sisters."

"But what happened to Joseph?" asked the Lieutenant quickly.

"There were two girls before him, Lieutenant, called Rachel and Leah. They were handy in the garden; the one planted and the other weeded. When the bishop paid a visit he declared he'd never tasted such peas and such strawberries. They married, too; each of them got a foundry owner. And now I'm coming to Joseph."

"He became a squire, I suppose?" said the Lieutenant.

"He became a tenant of his father's," the *jungfru* corrected him. "He looked after the fields and tended the cows and provided food for his parents and his brethren."

"H'm—that was just what I thought." So saying, the Lieutenant arose and sidled toward the door, where his hat and cane were hanging, and sneaked out.

"The thirteenth was David," pursued the *jungfru*. "He married three times, and had three children by each wife. If it please you, I can tell you the names of all the wives and children. . . . But maybe 'twould be better to keep to the twenty brethren?"

They all thought that quite the wisest plan. But with these prospects before her, Fru Lagerlöf felt a bit uneasy.

"I'll run out and fetch something to work on," she said, "then I'll be able to follow you better." But it was a good while before she came back with that work.

"The fourteenth was a girl named Deborah. She was always so nice about giving me a hand with the bread-making. She never got married and never left home, for she had to stay at the deanery and help me and her mother with the little ones. Sometimes she was kind of queer, though, and then she'd say she liked the Catholic religion because it didn't allow its priests to marry."

A slight noise was heard down by the door. Herr Tyberg had slipped out so softly no one noticed it till he was gone.

"The fifteenth was a girl, and her name was Martha. She was the greatest beauty you ever set eyes on! But she, too, was a bit queer. When she came seventeen she married a dean who was two-and-sixty, just because she wanted to get away from home."

Here Anna and Johan stood up. They must go fetch a light, they said. It was some little time before that light was brought.

"The sixteenth was called Mary. She was homely, and she used to say she'd never be able to catch a parson or a gentleman; but she was that eager to leave home she took up with a farm-hand, and went off and got married."

Mamselle Lovisa remained faithfully at her post, where she had gone sound asleep; but this the *jungfru* had not noticed.

"The seventeenth was hardly eighteen when she moved away from the deanery. She used to help the missus write letters to all the brothers and sisters; for that was more than any one body could do."

The door opened ever so little and shut again.

"The eighteenth," droned the *jungfru*, "was but fifteen when he declared he was going to America because he couldn't put up with so many relatives.

"And number nineteen and twenty, they were only fourteen and thirteen when I last saw them."

At that moment Fru Lagerlöf came in with her knitting, Anna appeared with the lamp, and Mamselle Lovisa awoke.

"Thanks, thanks, dear Jungfru Anna," said Fru Lagerlöf. "We shall never forget this. It has been so very instructive to me and my children."

VI

THE BRIDAL-CROWN

MAMSELLE LOVISA LAGERLÖF used to dress the brides. Not all the girls in the parish who married came to her to be decked, only the daughters of the best peasant families. Some years there were two or three brides, and some none at all.

Formerly, when Mårbacka was a parsonage, it had been the duty of the pastor's womenfolk to deck the brides, especially those who were to be married in the church.

Mamselle Lovisa's mother and maternal grandmother and great-grandmother before her had performed this same service. It was an old custom which had been handed down.

She had inherited all the old bridal trumpery which in the course of time had accumulated at Mårbacka. She had a large old cupboard, in a drawer of which were treasured long strings of glass, coral, and amber beads, a collection of tortoise-shell combs that stood up eight inches from the head, and half-round pasteboard forms, covered either with stiff white satin or hand-painted flowers, in use at the period when coifs were worn.

She had also a high pasteboard bridal-crown, the points of which were covered partly with gilt paper and partly with pink-and-green taffeta. There were wreaths of artificial roses and yards on yards of green satin ribbon sewn with flowers of pink satin. In the same drawer there were Jenny-Lind-ringlets, to be fastened on so as to fall against the face, hair pins with dangle-buttons, long ear-pendants of imitation pearls, an assortment of brass brooches, bracelets, and shoe buckles set with glass rubies, amethysts, and sapphires.

In the days when these things were in vogue it was a responsible and laborious task to deck a bride. For days before the wedding the bride dresser had to sit sewing flowered satin bands round the skirt and sleeves of the wedding dress. Sometimes the crown had to have fresh gilt paper and there were paper flowers to be made, and all the brass things had to be polished till they shone like gold.

Though all the gewgaws were shoddy stuff, a peasant-bride with a high crown and a broad flower wreath on her head, with strand on strand of multi-colored beads hanging down from her neck, with flowered satin sash round her waist, with a band of gay ribbon bordering her skirt, with bangled wrists and buckled shoes, must have been the most dazzling sight one could behold.

And it was also the most becoming array for a tall, bright-eyed, rosy-cheeked peasant lass, whose figure had been developed by hard toil and whose skin was tanned by sun and wind. Thus arrayed, she carried herself with dignity and pride, as if for a space she were exalted above her kind. To the bridegroom on the wedding day she looked a queen, a veritable goddess of riches. She was the most gorgeous flower in all the meadow, and to his eyes she glittered like a jewelled casket.

When Mamselle Lovisa dressed brides the old frippery was no longer in use. Now it had to be a natty little crown of myrtle, a thin wreath, also of myrtle, and a long white veil. Sometimes she would put a band of red satin ribbon round the waist of a plain black dress, and lend her brides her own gold brooch, gold bracelets, and watch and chain, to relieve at least a little the severity of the attire.

She must indeed have sighed for the olden times, and felt that something was lost by being so sparing with colours and ornaments, by concealing the rugged, and sometimes rather coarse, features of the peasant brides behind a sheer, white veil. That mode suited better the pale delicate city maiden, who wished to appear before the bridegroom as something ethereal and dreamlike. She conceded that this, too, was a pretty fashion; but certainly the peasant brides would have looked much better in the old, characteristic array.

Besides, it was difficult to procure fresh myrtle for the wreath and crown. Mamselle Lovisa tried to raise a little myrtle herself, but somehow it never seemed to grow for her, and the brides rarely had any to help out with.

Once Mamselle Lovisa got into trouble. A middle-aged woman, one Kaisa Nilsdotter, came and asked her if she would not dress her as bride. The woman was of the poorer peasant class, while the prospective husband was a schoolmaster. She felt that since she was making such an advantageous marriage no less a person than Mamselle Lagerlöf should deck her. And Mamselle Lovisa was quite willing. All she asked was that the bride should help her find the myrtle.

"I am nearly out of myrtle," she said, "and do not know where to procure any."

The woman agreed to furnish the myrtle for both crown and wreath. The day before the wedding she sent a few twigs with leaves so blackened and damaged they could hardly be used for a bridal crown.

Here was a dilemma! Mamselle Lovisa stripped her own myrtles of every bit of green; but this did not go very far. The maids ran over to see what they could find on the neighbouring farms, and came back with only a few poor sprigs. All the myrtle seemed to be sick that year; the leaves were black, and dropped off if one but touched them.

It would never do to bind any green but myrtle into a bridal-crown. Nice, fresh whortleberry is very like myrtle; but to wear a bridal-crown of whortleberry green would be a terrible disgrace. The bride might actually think she was not properly married.

Mamselle Lovisa laid the miserable little twigs in water to freshen them a bit, and worked far into the night on the wreath and crown. It looked a hopeless task, but she made the best of it. In the morning she quietly slipped out to the woods, but returned as she had gone—empty handed. Passing through the kitchen to her room she averred that never had she had such difficulty trying to bind a pretty bridal-crown. The maids felt sorry for her, and offered to run to still other cottages to beg myrtle.

"No, thank you," she said, "it's too late now. The bride and groom may be here at any moment."

She went into her room and stuck a few more leaves into the crown and wreath where they were the barest, then showed her work to the housekeeper and the maids.

"How in the world did you do it, Mamselle Lovisa!" one exclaimed. "Why, that wreath and crown are just as pretty as those you usually make, though 'twas mostly bare sprigs and black leaves you had."

Mamselle Lovisa then explained that she had freshened the leaves in water, it was only smoke and dust that had blackened them.

Shortly afterwards the bridal pair arrived. The bride was decked in Mamselle Lovisa's room. Though no longer young, the woman had a good and pleasing appearance. When she was all ready Mamselle Lovisa conducted her into the parlour, that she might view herself in the large mirror. And she was delighted.

"I never would have thought I could look that well!" she said. Then she took out a bottle of cologne and a pretty box—gifts from the groom. The box was filled with small candies, loaf-sugar, raisins, and lozenges. These she passed round—first to Mamselle Lovisa, then to the others. All had to dab themselves with a few drops of the cologne and take a piece of candy or a raisin from the box. She looked more pleased and happy than the young brides usually did, and every one complimented her on her appearance.

In a few moments she and the bridegroom drove off to the parsonage to be married, and from there to the bride's home, to celebrate.

For a time Kaisa Nilsdotter was very happy in her married life. Although her husband was much older than she, her respect for his learning was so great that she took special pride in ministering to his comfort and in making him a pleasant home. Then a rumour got afloat. It must have been started by some person at Mårbacka; but who the author was none could say. At all events, it travelled round the whole parish. At last some kind friend no doubt whispered it into the ear of Kaisa Nilsdotter.

"Mamselle Lovisa Lagerlöf bound your bridal-crown with whortleberry green."

At first she would not believe it. Such a thing was beyond credence. But after a while she began to think back. Her bridal-crown had been as pretty as anyone else's. It had looked so fresh and green on her head. She remembered how proud she had been because a fine Mamselle had put it on her. But was the crown not much too green? The spring she was married the myrtle had all been poor, she remembered, for she had tried in vain to find some green sprays. Maybe Mamselle Lovisa had thought it was not necessary to be so very particular with one who came of such humble folk? She would never have dared offer a crown of whortleberry to the daughter of a squire.

She brooded over this and talked with her husband about it. She wondered whether they were really married, in case it was true that her crown had been of whortleberry green.

The husband tried to reason with her, but she wept and was utterly wretched, thinking herself disgraced and humiliated. Mamselle Lovisa had thought she was not fine enough to be dressed by her, so she had made her a crown of whortleberry, and now she and all the parish were laughing at her. Her husband finally advised her to go to Mårbacka and ask Mamselle Lovisa herself about it.

She chanced to come at a most inopportune time. There was a grand party that day at Mårbacka, and when she stepped into the kitchen the maids were too busy to give her more than a short how-do-you-do. She asked for Mamselle Lovisa, who was inside with her guests, and they would not call her out. She would have to excuse them, too, for there was such a lot of company to serve. But, if she liked, she might step into Mamselle Lovisa's room, and wait there for her; which she did.

It was here the crown had been placed on her head. She remembered how happy she was that day, and now it was hard to believe there had been any deception.

Presently two maids passed through the room, each carrying a tray of filled wine glasses. They left the door ajar so that she could see into the dining room and parlour, which were full of people. It was indeed a big party, she thought. In there were not only the gentry of Ämtervik, but the Dean's and the Doctor's folk from Sunne and Pastor Hammargren of Karlstad —the husband of Mamselle Lovisa's sister. Feeling rather embarrassed, she went to shut the door, when she caught a few words that made her stop and listen.

Lieutenant Lagerlöf, with wine glass in hand, stood in the middle of the floor announcing the betrothal of his sister Lovisa to Pastor Milén, the clergyman at Ämtervik.

Then there was much toasting and congratulating. Everyone looked happy and pleased, which was not surprising. Mamselle Lovisa was a woman of forty, and her relatives had hardly expected that she would marry. Pastor Milén was a widower with four small children who needed a mother's care. It was all so right and fitting.

Kaisa Nilsdotter had heard that when Mamselle Lovisa was young she would not marry because she had not the heart to leave her parents. But now that they were dead she wanted a home of her own. She had also heard that Mamselle Lovisa did not care to go far from

Mårbacka, and, happily, the parsonage was but five minutes' walk from there.

It sort of cut into Kaisa Nilsdotter that everything should go so well for Mamselle Lovisa—she who had made a whortleberry crown for her. Stepping back from the doorway, she saw the old housekeeper, who had come in to hear the betrothal announcement, standing just behind her. Kaisa Nilsdotter laid a heavy hand on the housekeeper's shoulder.

"I came here to find out whether Mamselle Lovisa made my bridal-crown of whortleberry green," she said. "But maybe 'twouldn't do to ask her about it on a day like this?"

The housekeeper was rather startled, but she was not one to be easily thrown off her guard.

"How can you say anything so idiotic, Kaisa!" she flouted. "Everyone in the house knows what a lot of bother Mamselle Lovisa had with your bridal-crown. We all ran about to every cottage around here, and begged the myrtle."

Kaisa stared at her as if searching her very soul to get at the truth. "But the whole parish says so," she declared.

The old housekeeper, whose sole thought was to pacify the woman and get her out of the house, lest she disturb Mamselle Lovisa on this of all days, said:

"But I tell you, Kaisa, that as sure as Mamselle Lovisa's own bridal-crown will be of myrtle was yours of myrtle, and of nothing else."

"I'll bear those words in mind," said Kaisa. "And when I see what Mamselle Lovisa's bridal-crown is bound with, then I'll know how it was with mine."

"You can rest easy as to that," the housekeeper assured her.

The two then went into the kitchen, and Kaisa, looking quite calm now, put out her hand in farewell.

"I may as well be going," she said. "Anyhow, I don't suppose I could see Mamselle Lovisa to-day to speak to."

With that she was off. The housekeeper went back to her work, and, in the rush and excitement, forgot about the woman. It was not till a day or two afterward that she told Mamselle Lovisa what Kaisa Nilsdotter had said and what she herself had replied.

Mamselle Lovisa went white as a sheet.

"Oh, Maja!" she cried, "how could you say that! It would have been better to tell her that I put a few little sprays of whortleberry green in her crown."

"I had to ease her mind to get her to go," the housekeeper explained.

"And so you said my crown would be of myrtle as surely as hers was. Now you'll see, Maja, there will be no bridal-crown for me!"

"Oh, you'll be married right enough, Mamselle Lovisa. Pastor Milén is not the man to jilt you."

"Who knows? Something else might come up to prevent it."

Mamselle Lovisa worried over this a few days, and

then let it pass out of mind. She had other things to think of. In six months the wedding was to take place, and she must begin at once on the household linens and the trousseau.

She set up looms, sewed, and worked monograms. She finally went to Karlstad to shop, and returned with the fabric for a wedding dress and a little wire frame of a crown, to be bound with myrtle. She did not wish to use the old frame worn by so many brides, but wanted a bridal-crown of her own.

But these purchases had no sooner been made than the unexpected happened. Pastor Milén became ill and was confined to his bed a long time. When he recovered sufficiently to be up and about he seemed strangely changed. People noticed that he did not care to talk with his betrothed, and never went the short distance to Mårbacka to see her. When summer came he went away to a health resort. During his long absence he never once wrote to Mamselle Lovisa. It was a time of anxiety and distress for her. She inferred from his silence that he wished to break with her, and sent him back his ring. The day this happened she said to the old housekeeper:

"Now you see, Maja, that my bridal-crown will not be bound with myrtle, either."

*　　*　　*

One day, many years later, one of the young daughters of Lieutenant Lagerlöf asked her Aunt Lovisa to

lend her some of the old peasant bridal things to dress
up in. Mamselle Lovisa gave her the key to the cupboard where the old treasures were kept and which had
long since been removed to the storeroom upstairs.

The young girl unlocked the cupboard and pulled
out a drawer. She gazed at the contents in astonish-
ment. Before her lay not the usual gaudy trumpery,
but only a parcel of tulle, some coloured satin fabric,
and a little wire form of a bridal-crown. She saw at
once that she had opened the wrong drawer, the bridal
things were in the next one. Just the same, she stood a
moment looking into the drawer. It wrung her heart
to think that poor, unhappy Aunt Lovisa had never
come to use the things lying there. She knew that for
years her aunt had grieved in silence, and would not be
comforted. Then something came back to memory.
One day during the saddest period of her aunt's unhappiness she had gone into her room and had found her
sitting before a heap of whortleberry green, a little wire
crown in her hand. Her aunt had cut off a few sprays
and was binding them round the crown, when Fru
Lagerlöf came in.

"Why, Lovisa, whatever are you doing?" she had
asked with a frightened look on her face.

"I was thinking," Mamselle Lovisa had said, dream-
ily, "that if I would be content with a crown of whortle
—— But that's stupid!"

Then she had quickly jumped up, brushed aside the
crown and the leaves, and cried out: "I know it's all

ended." Then pacing the floor and wringing her hands
the while, she had moaned: "There's no help for it
now."

"But, my dear Lovisa, it was only on account of his
illness," Fru Lagerlöf had answered.

Mamselle Lovisa had continued to pace up and down,
up and down, in anguish and despair.

"If only I hadn't put whortleberry in Kaisa Nilsdotter's bridal-crown!" she had wailed.

"Come, come, Lovisa, you mustn't think that."
Just then Fru Lagerlöf had caught sight of the child
standing there, wide-eyed.

"Go into the other room, Selma," she had said.
"Aunt Lovisa has a sorrow, and you children must not
come here and disturb her."

VII

"VACKERFELDT"[1]

THE tinkle of a silver bell is heard from the road. Colour-Sergeant Karl von Wachenfeldt comes driving. . . .

Colour-Sergeant Karl von Wachenfeldt—was it not he who once on a time was proclaimed the handsomest man in Värmland, if not in all Sweden? Was it not he who was the idol of the Stockholm ladies the winter season of 1820, when he visited the Capital to take some sort of examination in land surveying? Was it not he who made up sleighing parties and led cotillions with a dash that put all the *beaux cavaliers* of the *haute monde* into the shade? Was it not he who danced so divinely and conversed so enchantingly that his fine relatives, who at first would not recognize the poor Värmland under-officer, finally sent him letters of invitation, couched in the humblest terms, because the young ladies could have no pleasure at a ball not graced by his presence?

And was it not he who had such astounding luck at the gaming-table it enabled him to live that winter in Stockholm like a Lieutenant of the Guard? Was it not

[1]Vacker is the Swedish for pretty or handsome.

155

he, by the way, who hobnobbed with counts and barons, and outshone them in gallantry and elegance? Was it not he who at a private theatrical in the home of Admiral Wachtmeister played the leading lover and sang his couplets so passionately that the next morning he found a score of love letters in his post-box? Was not he the first to drive through the streets of Stockholm with harness and trappings adorned with chimes of silver bells? Was it not he who was known to all Stockholm, so that wherever he appeared, whether at the Royal Gardens or the Blue Gate, at the Opera or among the moving throngs in the street, it was whispered: "Look! here comes *Vackerfeldt*. Oh—oh, see! Here comes *Vackerfeldt!*"

Was it not he who, after his one and only memorable winter in Stockholm, duplicated his triumphs at Karlstad and wherever else he chanced to be? Was it not he who, with Sergeant Sellblad as companion and Drummer Tyberg as valet, went down to Göteborg, where he passed himself off as a Finnish baron, and for a whole fortnight spoke with a Finnish accent, while running a gaming-house for the benefit of wealthy merchants' gay young sons? Was not he the only underofficer that had ever got to dance with the haughty Countess of Apertin? And was it not he who became so enamoured of the beautiful Mamselle Widerström, when she sang in *La Preciosa* at the Karlstad theatre, that he abducted her and would have got over into Norway with her, had not her manager happily overtaken them at Arvika? And, finally, was it not he who came to Captain Wästfelt at Angersby as Adjutant something or other, and put life into the young folk in Fryksdalen? Were ever such grand fair balls, such merry Christmas feasts, such jolly crayfish parties, and such delightful wanderings to picturesque places of interest! The romantic wife of the Captain who lay on a couch all day reading novels, did she not find in him the embodiment of her heroes of romance? And her young daughters, were not their first love dreams of him?

On the neighbouring place, Mårbacka, where there was a houseful of pretty daughters—what happened there? Could they resist a *beau cavalier* who manipulated the curling-tongs as skilfully as he did the guitar, and had the nimbus of Amor shining above his fair, curled hair?

* * *

Colour-Sergeant von Wachenfeldt comes driving down the rocky road, while the lone silver bell tinkles feebly and almost mournfully. In the days of his power and glory the sixty silver bells which hung from the harness and trappings jingled right merrily. They had, so to speak, rung in his triumphs, had heralded the coming of a conqueror. But now when there is only one solitary bell, it seems merely to announce the approach of a man whose day of fortune and happiness is over.

The Colour-Sergeant rides behind his old horse, Kalle, which is so noticeably small that everyone he meets in the road turns to look after it. But, on the other hand, no one turns to look at the horse's owner.

Driving past Gunnarsby Inn, he sees two young girls standing at the well. He salutes them with a flourish of his whip, and from force of habit gives them one of his most seductive smiles, but receives in return an indifferent glance. The girls do not drop the well bucket in wonder, or stand rapt with cheeks aglow, to gaze after him.

Colour-Sergeant von Wachenfeldt gives his horse a lash of the whip. He is no fool. He knows that his hair is gray and his face full of wrinkles, that his moustache is thin and faded, that one eye is filmed with a gray cataract, while the other, having been operated upon, is distorted by a magnifying monocle. He knows that he is old and nothing to look at now; yet he feels that people should not entirely forget what he once was. True, he has no better home nowadays than two hired rooms at a farmhouse in Stor Kil Parish. His only possessions are a horse, a carriole, a sleigh, and a few pieces of furniture, and his only subordinate is a crotchety old serving woman. For all that, he thinks it should not be completely forgotten that once he was *Vackerfeldt*, the celebrated *Vackerfeldt*.

He sits there in a mangy old fur coat and a still shabbier seal-skin cap. He wears thick lynx mittens to protect his gouty hands, but the distorted joints are noticeable even through the thick mittens. Nevertheless it is he, Wachenfeldt—he who has held so many beautiful women in his arms! The memory of that none can take from him. Who else in these parts has lived such a life and been so adored?

Pressing his lips together he tells himself he has nothing to regret. If he could live his life over again he would have it the same. All that youth and health and good looks can give a man he has enjoyed—love and adventure in fullest measure.

One thing perhaps Colour-Sergeant von Wachenfeldt wishes he had left undone. He should not have married Anna Lagerlöf, the noblest woman he had ever known. He had loved her madly, but he never should have espoused her.

Was it fitting that a *Vackerfeldt* should settle down to the prudent management of a farm and not try to harvest gold in some easier and pleasanter way? If his wife was adorable, must he needs think her the only adorable one? Could he change his nature by marrying? Was it not through his success as gambler and lover he had won his fame?

Yes, he regrets his marriage. His wife was not suited to him, but he concedes that she was too good for him. She had wanted orderliness, industry, tranquillity, and comfort, and had worn herself out trying to make a home for them, such as she had had at Mårbacka.

Others might think he should not so much regret

having married as having caused his wife grief and humiliation. After seventeen years of domestic infelicity, when Anna von Wachenfeldt could endure no more, she died. Then misfortunes of all sorts befell him. The creditors showed no further indulgence, but took away his home. He had to give up gambling, for now he lost as soon as he touched a card. The gout had also come, and the gray cataract. Before he had reached sixty he was white-haired, stiff-jointed, half-blind, helpless, and poverty-stricken. It would have been no small comfort to him now to have had his good, loving wife still with him.

Since her death he had been cut off from all social intercourse. No one cared whether he lived or died. None invited him to their homes. It looked as if people had merely tolerated him for his wife's sake. When he yearns for laughter and merriment, when he would like to sit down to a well-served dinner and talk with cultured people, he has no place to go. When the holidays come round, with their long leisure hours, when he would like to escape from the deadly monotony of the farmhouse, he does not know what to do with himself.

There is just one place in the world where he can go for a bit of a taste of the old life, and that place is Mårbacka, whence he had brought his wife. He knows what they think and feel there—that he had made her life very unhappy. They actually believe that he tormented her to death. Nevertheless, he journeys thither thrice a year for the great holiday festivities. But for these visits to Mårbacka his life would be intolerable.

The silver bell rings out a loud plaint. The Colour-Sergeant has just dealt his little horse a stinging blow. Life has many bitter fruits, which one must take. It seems quite proper that the horse should share the pain of his master.

*   *   *

If the little Mårbacka children had not known by any other signs that Christmas was at hand, they would have guessed it when Colour-Sergeant von Wachenfeldt appeared.

They were overjoyed when they saw his horse and cutter coming up the driveway. They raced through the house shouting the glad tidings, and rushed out on the steps to greet him, crying Good-day and Welcome. They fetched bread for his horse and carried his lean carpet-bag, embroidered in cross-stitched leaves and flowers, down to the Lieutenant's office, which the Sergeant was to occupy.

It was remarkable that the children were always so glad to see Colour-Sergeant von Wachenfeldt, for he never brought them any goodies or presents. But they must have thought him a part of Christmas, which no doubt accounted for their joy. Anyhow, it was well they were friendly, for the grown folk made no ado over him. Fru Lagerlöf and Mamselle Lovisa did not go out to receive the guest, and it was with rather a heavy sigh the Lieutenant put down his Värmland News, and arose from his rocker to go and meet him.

"Well, well, so you're here again, Wachenfeldt!" he said, as he stood on the steps. After putting a few queries as to the state of the roads and the journey, he conducted his brother-in-law to his room, where he cleared out a drawer of his chiffonier and made place in the wardrobe; then he went off with his children, leaving the guest to himself.

With each visit of the Colour-Sergeant memories of the Lieutenant's dead sister became more and more poignant. She was the eldest child; she had cared for him when he was a little chap, had dressed and undressed him, and coddled him. He had loved her best of all his sisters, had been more proud of her than of the others. And then she had to go and fall in love with a worthless fellow like this Wachenfeldt! She was both beautiful and noble, and as good and true as she looked. She had always been sunny, and had brightened the lives of those about her. She had striven to the last breath to keep her home; the husband had only wasted and squandered. She would not let her family know how hard she had it, lest they should come to her aid. So she broke under the strain when she was barely forty.

It was a sad and distressing tale, and the Lieutenant, while this was seething in him, could not be cordial to Von Wachenfeldt; he had therefore to take a long walk to let his indignation cool a bit.

Fru Lagerlöf and Mamselle Lovisa felt much as he

did. Anna Wachenfeldt had been the favourite sister-in-law of Fru Lagerlöf, who had looked up to her with genuine admiration. Anna had been the one to welcome her most heartily into the family, and she could never forgive Colour-Sergeant von Wachenfeldt for making this beloved woman unhappy.

Mamselle Lovisa, as a child, had made long visits at Valsäter, the home of the Wachenfeldts, and knew more about her sister's troubles than any of them. She could never hear the name Wachenfeldt without thinking of a certain morning when a couple of strange men came to Valsäter and led from the barn the two best cows. Her sister had run out and asked them what they were doing there, and they had coolly answered that the Sergeant the night before had staked the cows in a game with their master, and lost. Mamselle Lovisa saw her sister as it were before her, and remembered how distressed she had been over this. "He will never come to his senses," she had said, "until he has made an end of me."

However, Mamselle Lovisa was the first to think of her duties as hostess. She got up from the sewing table, where she had been embroidering and betimes taking little peeps into a novel that lay open in her sewing basket, and went to the kitchen door.

"Maja dear," she called to the housekeeper, apologetically, "now we have Wachenfeldt here again!"

"I can't understand why that fellow, who was so mean to his wife, is allowed to come here at every holiday time," the housekeeper retorted with considerable asperity.

"But one can't very well drive him away," pleaded Mamselle Lovisa. "And now, Maja, please put the coffeepot on, so that he'll have something to warm him a bit after his long, cold drive."

"Why must he always come just when you've all had your coffee and the fire's gone dead in the stove!" The housekeeper looked as if she were not going to make a move.

But the coffeepot must have got on somehow, for shortly afterward the housemaid went down to the office and bade Colour-Sergeant von Wachenfeldt come to the living room for coffee.

In crossing the yard to the house, he walked with the aid of a cane, which he put by in the outer hall, and carried himself fairly well as he came into the room. Mamselle Lovisa, who stood there to receive him, noticed all the same that he had difficulty in walking. When she took his hands she felt how swollen they were, and when she looked up into his face, his distorted eye stared at her horribly. Then a good part of her resentment vanished. She thought to herself that he had already received his punishment, and she was not going to add woe to woe.

"It was nice that Wachenfeldt could come to us again this Christmas," she forced herself to say. Whereupon she poured him some coffee and he went over to his accustomed place, between the porcelain stove and the folded card table. It was a modest corner, and also the warmest in the room. The Colour-Sergeant knew what he was about when he chose that seat.

He at once began telling Mamselle Lovisa about his servant, Inga, and her constant quarrels and fights with the peasants who owned the farm where he lived. He knew that such petty gossip amused his sister-in-law, and did not fail to observe that she presently poured herself a cup of coffee so as to keep him company.

Dusk had fallen while they chatted over their coffee cups, a light was brought and placed on the round table over by the sofa, soon after which Fru Lagerlöf appeared.

She had not conquered her feeling of aversion, and it was a cool reception the Colour-Sergeant got from her; she barely touched his hand, but did not speak, and then sat down to her work.

The Colour-Sergeant, who calmly went on talking to Mamselle Lovisa, quickly changed the topic of conversation. He told about some strange cases of sickness among the people and the animals on the farm, which he had succeeded in curing.

Here was something that interested Fru Lagerlöf; it was in her line. Before she knew it, she had been drawn into the conversation.

Finally the Lieutenant came in and sank into his rocker. At first he was silent and depressed. But now, without anyone's quite knowing how it came about, the conversation drifted in another direction. It carried back to old Karlstad, where the Colour-Sergeant was born and the Lieutenant went to school, and of which the latter loved to talk. Then it swung up to Stockholm, and took in Emilie Högquist, Jenny Lind, and much else of a by-gone day that was beautiful and memorable. At last they fell to telling old Värmland tales, and the evening passed so quickly they were all astonished when the maid came in to lay the table for supper.

The amazing thing about it all was that when Colour-Sergeant von Wachenfeldt related any of his personal experiences he invariably stood out as the wisest and most prudent man one could wish to meet. That he had taken part in many adventures and exploits was true enough, but he had always played the rôle of the counselling friend who helped stupid folk out of their scrapes.

Just to mention the Wästfelts of Angersby: what a staff he had been to these nice, childish persons! Particularly at the time when the son's intended threw him over and announced her engagement to another. No man ever spoke with greater veneration of his mother or his wife. Such a model son and devoted husband all might wish to have. He had always talked sensibly to young women, smoothed out lovers' quarrels, and welded together marriage bonds that threatened to break asunder. All the unhappy ones had made a confidant of him, and he had never betrayed them. He had even saved men seized with the gambling fever, had talked them to rights and reminded them of their duties.

After supper, when Von Wachenfeldt had limped down to his room, Lieutenant Lagerlöf, his wife and sister sat staring at each other—dumbfounded.

"Oh, that Wachenfeldt!" the Lieutenant exclaimed. "He's a wonder; he knows more than all of us put together."

"It is always a pleasure to talk with Wachenfeldt," said Mamselle Lovisa.

"If it is true that he has been so helpful to others, then how does it happen that he has managed his own affairs so badly?" queried Fru Lagerlöf, dryly.

"Some folks are like that," the Lieutenant averred.

*   *   *

Thenceforth, Colour-Sergeant von Wachenfeldt "feasted right royally," as is said in *Fritiof's Saga*— throughout the Christmas holidays, playing the wise and all-knowing old man. One could get his advice on almost everything. He could prescribe for pimples and the snuffles, give counsel in matters of dress, write recipes for cooking and dyeing, give instruction in agriculture, and offer the best and cleverest judgments of people. They appealed to him to settle knotty problems.

"Doesn't Wachenfeldt think it strange these children cannot be induced to eat carrots?" Mamselle Lovisa once put to him.

Colour-Sergeant von Wachenfeldt rose to the occasion.

"Wake me in the middle of the night and offer me carrots, and I'll eat."

It was positively unnatural his being so reasonable and practical. The dashing cavalier of old, the conquering hero with the sixty silver bells, was apparently no more.

Then it happened that Lieutenant Lagerlöf during one of Wachenfeldt's visits got into an argument with the ladies about a young girl in the district. Fru Lagerlöf and Mamselle Lovisa both thought her sweet and winsome, while the Lieutenant declared that no man could ever fall in love with her. He appealed the case in point to Wachenfeldt, as was the custom in the family.

"Tell me, Wachenfeldt, you who are a judge of women—would you kiss such a little Miss Snippit?"

Colour-Sergeant von Wachenfeldt, old as he was, flushed. He struck the table with his fist, half-rose from his seat, and thundered:

"Don't ask me such a thing! I have never kissed a homely woman."

The ungodly persons round him broke into hilarious shrieks. Here he had been acting the part of the sage and the plain man of common sense, yet a simple little query like that had unmasked him. The old *beau cavalier* still survived in him. Sick and wretched, old and dilapidated as he was, let none think or assume that he would kiss a plain woman.

O *Vackerfeldt! Vackerfeldt!*

VIII

IT WAS an impromptu orchestra that played that day at Mårbacka. There was Major Ehrencrona, a Finn by birth, who in former days had lived in a palatial home and been a *grand seigneur*, but who now in his old age occupied a rented room at a farmhouse, where he led a dull and monotonous existence, much like that of Colour-Sergeant von Wachenfeldt. He was reputed to be a master of the French horn; but since he had become poor and lonely he had not been heard to play.

And there was Herr Tyberg, who began life as drummer-boy with the Värmland Regiment and who surely would have killed himself with drink, had not the Lieutenant at Mårbacka, by a mere chance, discovered the man's special aptitude for teaching small children, and engaged him as tutor for his own little ones, and later found him a position as teacher in the elementary school at East Ämtervik.

Then, there was Jan Asker, who had also been in the regiment band, but who was now church-beadle and grave-digger at East Ämtervik. He came of an old family of musicians, and used to play the clarinet at all the peasant weddings and dances. His was an embittered and restless spirit. The only thing that reconciled him to life was music.

And there was the foundry bookkeeper, Geijer, who lived in the attic of the school building, and kept house for himself. He was passionately fond of music, but being too poor to provide himself with any sort of instrument, he had painted a keyboard on a common deal table, at which he sat and "played."

Then, too, there was Sexton Melanoz, who had received instruction from Dean Fryxell himself, and could scribble verse, cobble shoes, mend furniture, and run a farm. He was the star entertainer at all the weddings and wakes, and was moreover the best schoolmaster in the whole of Fryksdalen. Every Sunday morning he had to play the wheezy organ at the Ämtervik church, which he never could have endured if he'd not had his violin to console him on Sunday afternoons, for he was a musical soul.

These five had arranged to meet at Mårbacka on a certain day during the Christmas season, while there was still something left of the Christmas ale, the Christmas ham, and spiced bread.

The first to arrive did not go straight to the house, but waited till all were there. Whereupon they fell into line, the Major in the lead, and marched up to the front porch singing *Portugal, Spanjen, Stora Britanjen.*

Lieutenant Lagerlöf had perhaps some notion as to

what was in the air, but he had remained inside so as not to spoil the fun for the guests. But on hearing that song, he jumped up and ran out to greet them. Nor was Colour-Sergeant von Wachenfeldt, who was still at Mårbacka, long to follow.

When the visitors had gone down to the farm-office to remove their pelts and leggings, the Lieutenant sent his two boys, Daniel and Johan, up to the attic to fetch the guitar, the French horn, the flute, and the triangle, while he himself rushed into the bedroom and pulled his violin from under the bed; placing it on a chair, he unlocked the case and reverently uncovered the violin, which lay wrapped in a red silk handkerchief.

Though the Lieutenant himself never smoked or permitted others to smoke in the house, he sent the boys down to the office to fetch the old long-stemmed pipe, which had been there since Pastor Wennervik's time, and also a little square box filled with tobacco, so that Major Ehrencrona might have his usual smoke, to keep him in good humour.

When the five guests, the Colour-Sergeant, and the Lieutenant went into the living room, when the toddy-tray had been brought, and hot drinks made for all— except Herr Tyberg, of course, who had sworn off for good—and when the major had finally got his pipe to draw, they decided it was not worth while to pass the evening at card-playing or in small-talk, but they would have some music.

It was this the Lieutenant had anticipated; so now

he went for the instruments he had hurriedly assembled. His violin he offered to Sexton Melanoz, who most humbly protested that there were those in the room far more worthy than he to handle this, the greatest of all musical instruments. But when none claimed the distinction, he was as pleased as if he had suddenly come into a fortune, and at once proceeded to tune up.

The flute went to Herr Tyberg, of course. It had been his instrument in the regiment, when he had outgrown the drum. He was well acquainted with the old flute at Mârbacka, and knew it to be always dry and leaky. So he ran out to the kitchen to dip the flute in pale beer and bind it round with tow, to make it hold together.

The guitar was handed to Bookkeeper Geijer, who had a long thin face, a long slender neck, limpid blue eyes, and long slim fingers. There was a certain wistfulness about him, a sort of languishing grace. With a little girlish laugh, he strung the guitar-ribbon round his neck and tenderly pressed the instrument to his heart, as if embracing a sweetheart. The guitar had only three strings, but they were enough for him who was wont to perform on nothing better than a deal table.

Church-beadle Asker had had the foresight to bring his own clarinet. It was in the back pocket of his greatcoat, so that he had only to go down to the office and fetch it.

Colour-Sergeant von Wachenfeldt, sitting in his usual corner by the fire, tried to put on a good face, though he could not perform on any musical instrument with his gout-stiffened fingers. But the Lieutenant now went over to him with the triangle, which he could manage with ease. So the Colour-Sergeant, too, was happy.

Major Ehrencrona sat blowing smoke through his big white moustache. He saw how one after another had been provided with an instrument, but feigned indifference.

"Just give me a couple of pot-lids," he said to the Lieutenant, "so that I may at least join in the noise-making. I know, of course, that the instrument I play is not to be found in this house."

Like a streak, the Lieutenant darted into the parlour and came back with a brilliantly polished French horn, with green silk cord and tassel, he had managed to procure for the Major.

"What do you say to this, Uncle?" he asked him.

The old major beamed.

"Ha! you're a real fellow, Brother Eric Gustaf!" He put down his pipe and began to toot vociferously, sending out a volley of ear-splitting blasts.

Now that the guests were all furnished with instruments, they remarked that the host himself had none. Whereupon, the Lieutenant produced a little wooden whistle, one end of which must be placed in a glass of water when one blew upon it. By so doing one could make trills as sweet as any nightingale's.

And last, they begged Fru Lagerlöf to accompany them on the piano.

In honour of the Major they first essayed the stirring Finnish martial hymn, the "March of the Björneborgers." Fru Lagerlöf struck the opening chords, and the orchestra followed as best it could. It was a clang and a din that took the house by storm.

They did their best, all of them. Sexton Melanoz, Jan Asker, and Herr Tyberg played with a certain assurance, but the Major frequently lagged behind and the Lieutenant put in a few haphazard trills, due in part to the freakish behaviour of his "nightingale" and in part to a mischievous desire to throw the others out of time.

When they had played the march through once they were so enlivened and interested they wanted to go over it again, to get it quite perfect. The Major blew and tooted till his eyes were red and his cheeks distended, as if ready to split. Obviously, he was not as proficient at the horn as he had made himself out, for he did not play in time even on second trial.

Of a sudden he jumped up and hurled the French horn across the room toward the chimney corner with such force that it came near crushing Colour-Sergeant von Wachenfeldt's most sensitive toe.

"Hang it all!" he shouted. "I'm not going to sit here and spoil the Björneborgers' March. . . . Play on, you who can!"

The others were a bit disconcerted, naturally, but they took up the march for the third time. And now the Major sang, *Sons of a race that bled.* He carried the air in a deep, rich bass that filled the whole house. The human voice flowed on like a mighty tide, bearing along with it the tinny old piano, the shrill clarinet, the violin, scraped in old fiddler-fashion, the three-stringed guitar, the Sergeant's triangle and the Lieutenant's capricious nightingale.

Their hearts warmed, for the loss of Finland still rankled in their breasts; and now they seemed to be marching with the brave Björneborg lads to take back their country from the Russians.

When the march was finished the Lieutenant motioned to his wife, who struck up *Worthy Fathers, Noble Shadows*, from the opera of "Gustaf Vasa," which was the Major's great show piece. He rendered the song with power and feeling, and the instruments seemed almost to sing with him.

Over on the straight-backed sofa, quiet as mice, sat all the children—Daniel, Johan, Anna, Selma, and Gerda—listening. What could they do but keep still, when the grown-ups played and carried on like youngsters? When the Major sang Worthy Fathers, Noble Shadows, they thought he sang of himself and the others who were performing in the living room.

To the children they were all like ghosts of a vanished something—shadows of a great and glorious past of which they could but catch the faint gleams of an afterglow.

THE NEW MÅRBACKA

THE SEVENTEEN CATS

THERE was a cow-girl at Mårbacka named Britta Lambert, who had been on the place from the time of the Paymaster of the Regiment. She was little and ugly, with a face like old parchment, and she had only one eye. In the company of humans she was crabbed and surly, but she loved animals. If a cow was expected to calve in the night, she would make up a bed in the barn and sleep there. Every day she would heat water in the brew house and carry great bucketfuls down to the barn, so that the cows might have warm mash. When the hay ran low in the cow-house, along in April, and the cows had to chew on rye-straw, she was not above sneaking over to the stable and stealing hay from the horses.

The barn in which she ruled was very old and so dark you could scarcely see your hand before you; the passageways were narrow, the floor was worn full of holes, and the cows stood in cramped little stalls, which Britta did not think to keep clean. Nevertheless, steady contentment reigned in the old cow-house. There was no fear of a cow's overfeeding, or getting anything sharp in her fodder, or that aught would go wrong

with the calving. There were lots of calves and plenty
of milk. The mistress at Mårbacka never had any
anxiety concerning the cow-house.

But there was one species of animal Britta Lambert
loved even better than she loved the cow, and that was
the cat. She believed that cats had some sort of
supernatural power to protect her and her cattle. The
worst thing one could ask of her was to drown a kitten
now and then, lest there should be more cats than
cows to care for. When anyone stepped inside the dark
cow-house he was met on all sides by the uncanny gleam
of green cat-eyes. The cats got under his feet and
sprang on to his shoulders—for that Britta had got them
into the habit of doing.

When Lieutenant Lagerlöf took over Mårbacka, on
the death of his father, there were no less than seventeen
cats in the barn. They were all of the tortoise-shell
variety, with not a black or white or gray one among
them. For Britta Lambert believed it was only the
red cats that brought luck.

Now the Lieutenant was a great lover of animals,
and he had no antipathy whatever to cats; but to feed
and house seventeen of them in the barn—that, he
thought, was a bit too much. The cats, to be sure, were
vigilant hunters of rats and field-mice, but they also
pursued little birds; there was hardly so much as a
sparrow left at Mårbacka. Besides, the milk they
consumed would have fed three calves.

Anyway, it's a sorry business having to do away

with cats. So the Lieutenant, rather than distress Britta Lambert and the other womenfolk, said nothing to them about a certain plan he had in mind. He merely gave the wink to old Bengt, the former stableman, who still pottered round the place at this and that.

Then, in some mysterious way the cats began to disappear—not all at once, but by gradual elimination. Britta Lambert thought she noticed that one and another of her precious tabbies was missing, yet she was not quite sure about it, since the cats were all so much alike in colour and markings. She attempted to count them as they came up for their milk, but that was not so easy, for they pushed and crowded each other at the milk-trough. Then, too, it was almost pitch-dark in the barn. She complained to the old housekeeper and the young mistress.

"You see," she said, "'tis this I fear me, that if you do away with the red cats, you'll do away with the luck in the cow-house. No good can come to folks as begins by being ungrateful to them that's helped us all up to now."

Fru Lagerlöf and the housekeeper both assured her they had no evil designs upon her cats. They thought she would soon have them back again—the whole seventeen.

All the same, Britta noted that the cats were becoming fewer and fewer. She suspected this one and that one, but none would confess to guilt. The only one of whom she could never have believed anything so sinful as that he would harm a cat, was the Lieutenant. She knew that his mother had taught him better.

"This'll never do, Master," she said to the Lieutenant every time he came into the barn. "You don't know how worried I am! The cats are leaving me."

"I don't see but they're running in front of my feet the same as usual," the Lieutenant replied.

"If there be thirteen left, 'tis all and no more," wailed the cow-girl. "I'd hate to be standing in the shoes of the one that's doing this! And worst of all, the farm'll suffer for it."

Now in those days the Lieutenant was a strong young man and an ambitious, enterprising farmer. He had big plans for Mårbacka. The estate was not extensive, but the soil was rich and the fields, spreading in one continuous stretch of expanse, were level and clear of stones. It would be no fault of his if the farm did not some day become the finest in the whole Fryken Valley. He had money at his command, for his father-in-law, Squire Wallroth, who was a man of means, admired his son-in-law's initiative and enterprise, and gave him the support he needed.

The Lieutenant set about reparcelling the land for rotation of crops. He dug ditches a fathom deep for drainage, and sowed timothy and clover in the meadows, so that they would produce something besides wild flowers; he bought a threshing machine, which did away with their having to stand in a barn all winter beating out the grain with flails, and he also procured some tall, fine-bred cattle from the manors down by the Ness. He did not let the cows wander in the woods from spring to autumn, and half-starve, but sent them to pasture in the open meadow. Everything that could be thought of to enhance the value of the farm was done: he carried on protracted negotiations with the peasants on the west side of the dale for the purchase of lands adjoining his; he built cottages for his workmen, that they might have decent homes, with outbuildings and a bit of ground where they could keep a cow and a pig.

Nor were his labours in vain. Within a year the farm paid back all he had laid out on it. There was such a harvest of hay he hardly knew where to store it all for the winter. For every bushel of peas sown he got twenty bushels in return, and when he planted turnips the ground gave forth such a blessed abundance it was more than his own folk could gather in. So he sent word to the neighbours to come with horse and cart, and take home all the turnips they could dig.

However, there was one serious obstacle to this work of improving the farm, and that was the little river Ämtan, which meandered in all sorts of graceful bends and curves down in the dale, where his fields lay. Ordinarily, the stream was not much bigger than a forest brook, but as soon as there came a good fall of rain it overflowed its banks, converting his clover meadows and oat fields into little lakes.

The Lieutenant decided that something must be done about the river. Where it flowed through his own property he deepened its bed and straightened its course. But little good came of that, for the peasants who owned the land below Mårbacka let the river run on in its old tortuous, sluggish way. Whenever there was a heavy rain it flooded their acres as well as his.

What was the good of all his labour with the soil, if Ämtan could at any time wash away his haystacks and rye-shooks? He would never be able to develop his property as he wished until the river was mastered.

He talked with the neighbours, and they seemed to be in favour of having the river properly dredged. A surveyor was consulted, who drew, measured, and made calculations; after which the Lieutenant convened a meeting of all interested parties at the parish public room.

More than a few obstacles had been surmounted by the time he had got thus far along with the project. The morning he was to drive to the meeting he felt quite happy, thinking that now the most difficult part of the work had been accomplished. But as he was getting into his carriole, right in the middle of the seat sat one of the red barn cats staring blankly at him.

There was nothing strange in that, however. The barn cats all loved to ride. Britta Lambert had trundled them in her wheel-barrow from the time they were tiny kittens, and in that way they had become as fond of riding as children, and would jump into all the farm vehicles. But they were not in the habit of venturing into the family carriages.

"So you'd like to come along to the meeting, would you?" said the Lieutenant. "Scat!"

The cat deigned to take itself off, but not before it had given the Lieutenant a sardonic look that made him feel positively uncomfortable.

Between the stable and the road the Lieutenant had to pass through three gates. On each of the gateposts sat a red barn cat. Nor was there anything strange in that. Cats like to sit on gateposts to sun themselves and watch everything that moves on the ground below. But that morning the Lieutenant thought the cats all had a sinister look; they blinked at him as if they knew what would come of his trip. He was beginning to think Britta Lambert was right—that they were little witches and goblins in the guise of cats.

Now it is not a good omen to meet a lot of cats when one sets out on a journey, so the Lieutenant spat three times for each cat, as his mother had taught him to do, and thought no more about them during the drive. He went over in his mind the whole plan of the ditching and prepared himself to lay the proposition before the meeting clearly and convincingly.

But instantly the Lieutenant stepped inside the parish room, an unmistakable air of wariness and opposition assailed him. The peasants sat there immovable, with tight-shut faces. He began to surmise that they had changed their minds, which proved to be the case. All his arguments were overruled.

"We understand, of course, that this ditching would

be a good thing for Mårbacka," said their spokesman, "but it's of no importance to us."

When he came back from the meeting he felt rather depressed. The matter of the dredging was settled for some time to come. The river could go on creating havoc. If a stray herd of cattle trampled his fields he could drive them out, but the river must be left free to choke and destroy all in its path.

In the midst of these broodings on his frustrated hopes, he got up and went over to the servants' hall to see Bengt.

"It didn't go through, Bengt, that about the river," he said.

"That's too bad, Lieutenant!" the old man sympathized. "The Paymaster of the Regiment always said the farm would be worth twice as much if it wasn't for Ämtan."

"I say, Bengt"—the Lieutenant lowered his voice— "there aren't so many cats in the barn now, eh? . . . Perhaps we'd better let Britta keep what's left of them."

"Just as you wish, Lieutenant."

The Lieutenant lowered his voice a bit more, as if fearful lest the walls of the old manservants' room might hear what he said.

"Where did you drown them, Bengt?"

"I took 'em down to the river. I was afraid they'd come floating up and be seen, if I drowned them here in the duck pond."

"H'm, in the river—I thought so!" The Lieutenant

stood reflecting a long while. Suddenly he burst out: "There's a lot that's queer in this world!"

"Ay, there is that," old Bengt agreed.

As long as Lieutenant Lagerlöf lived he had to let the river do as it would with his fine fields. Year after year he saw it overflow its banks and spread out in innumerable lake-like ponds, from Mårbacka down through the whole dale. And every time it occurred he would tell about the red cats that sat on the gate-posts the morning he drove down to the meeting. Could it be possible that they knew how badly things would go for him? And was it true that one who did violence to a cat was punished? He wondered about that to the end of his days.

II

THE NEW BARN

LIEUTENANT LAGERLÖF wanted to have Mårbacka not only a productive and well-cared-for
farm, but a beautiful place, with stately ave-
nues of approach and extensive gardens of flowers and
shrubbery on all sides of the dwelling house.

Not far from the house stood the wretched old cow-
barn, with its thatched roof, its small window-openings,
and its weather-beaten timber walls. To be sure,
there was a row of century-old sycamores, with yellow,
lichen-clad trunks and a wealth of foliage, which concealed the building from view, so that the place was
perhaps not so very ugly after all. Still, the Lieutenant
declared he could never make Mårbacka look like a
manor until that cow-house was torn down.

The first few years he had been wholly occupied with
the cultivation of the soil; it was not till after the Strömstad visit and the death of Grandmother Lagerlöf
that he set about building the new barn, which had
to be finished before the old one could be pulled down.
That the new barn might not be easily seen from the
house, he decided to build it on the level meadow just
below the sand-hill, where the other outhouses stood.

When the womenfolk heard of this, a wail went up. Think of their having to go that long distance to tend the cows! And think how hard it would be on the cow-girl and the dairy-maid to have to carry the milk three times a day up the steep hill to the dairy! The Lieutenant turned a deaf ear. He was going to remove all the outbuildings and have everything of the sort, including the dairy, centred in the one place, thereby making it much easier for both serving-folk and animals.

The barn, though it would lie in an out-of-the-way spot, was going to be the finest in the whole district. It was to be built in the form of a cross, and of brick all the way up to the eaves-course, and would house at least fifty cows. It would only be lacking a spire to look like a church.

The Lieutenant discussed his building project with his father-in-law, Squire Wallroth, who had seen enough of the old cow-house to know that a new one was badly needed. He gave the Lieutenant quite a large sum of money for building purposes, and the latter immediately went ahead with the preliminary work. For two consecutive winters he quarried stone at Åsberget for the foundation; for two whole summers he had a clay-mill standing down by the duck pond, where the bricks were made and left to dry and harden in the sun; and for two autumns he had men at work in his own woodlands, cutting timber, that he might have proper material for cross-beams and rafters.

At last he was ready to stake out the ground and

start digging for the foundation. It was a great moment for him when the workmen put their spades to the ground to clear away the first layer of earth. They began the digging and foundation-laying on the east side, which was nearest the house. There all went well; the ground was firm and the stones stayed where they were put. But when they came to lay the stones on the west side, which gave on the field, they found that there had been a terrible miscalculation. They had not gone very deep before they came upon soft blue-clay, into which the stones sank and disappeared. The Lieutenant had made the grave mistake of not having the ground tested. But now that the foundation had been laid on one side, he thought it best to go on with the building in the place he had staked out. An old mason advised him to put the barn farther up toward the hill, as blue clay was treacherous stuff to build on. The Lieutenant would not hear of that. It would be all right, he said, to lay the foundation on blue clay; there must be a bottom even to that. As for stone to fill it in, well—there was the whole mountain range to take from.

Load after load of stone was dumped on to the clay and before long he had a wide stone dam there—solid and steady as could be—on which it seemed safe enough to lay a foundation. Then, one day, came a couple of heavy showers, and all at once cracks appeared in the dam. The next morning it began to sink, and in a few hours it was completely swallowed up.

But all summer the Lieutenant went on dumping stone into the clay, and when by autumn it was still uncertain whether the foundation would hold, he decided to put off the masonry work till the following year, in order to see how the blue clay would behave in the spring, when the frost was out of the ground.

As soon as the snow was gone, the Lieutenant went down to have a look at his wall. Yes, it was still there, no cracks in it. But then the regular spring thaw had not begun.

Every day, and many times a day, he went down to see how things were going. The wall remained intact, and the ground seemed now to be free of frost, so he ventured to send word to the master mason to come with his journeymen, and begin work.

They put up the walls on the north and east sides first, so as to give the insecure foundation on the west side time to settle. The latter part of June they began work on the doubtful side, and by the middle of July, when they had got almost up to the coping, they noticed some cracks in the wall. Then, all at once, the wall began to sag, and several layers of brick had to be torn down quickly, lest the whole wall give way.

Now things began to look serious for Lieutenant Lagerlöf. What to do next he did not know. By that time the money he had received from his father-in-law was used up. But Squire Wallroth, who was both open-handed and reasonable, would no doubt have let him have an additional sum, had he written and explained why the building would cost more than he had estimated. But after this fresh cave-in he felt loath to write. He would have to confess that as yet the barn had neither roof nor floor, that the walls were not even finished and that he must start laying a new foundation. His father-in-law would surely think he had shown poor judgment, and lose confidence in him.

The Lieutenant almost felt like giving up the whole building scheme—yet, somehow, the mere thought of it went against him. So many of his projects had come to naught, and, besides, the old cow-house was beyond repair.

Of course he should have started building on another spot long ago. But how could he do so now, when the walls were half-finished? It was a question which would entail the lesser outlay—to start building in a new place or continue at the old one.

At East Ämtervik lies a small foundry estate known as Gårdsjö, which is about three English miles from Mårbacka. Living there at that time was a brother of Fru Lagerlöf, Iron Master Karl Wallroth, a wise and prudent man on whose judgment the Lieutenant relied implicitly. To him he went for advice. Iron Master Wallroth counselled him by all means to dismiss the whole matter from his mind.

"It would be foolish to ask Father for more money to put into your building scheme," he said. "He's always ready to give one a lift, but he wants to see the money used to good advantage. And to put a mortgage on the estate in order to finish your barn would not be advisable. No telling how many times the work will have to be done over. You might lose all you have by it."

Afterward, the Lieutenant sat talking the whole evening with the brother-in-law and his wife, who insisted on his staying for supper. He tried to be his usual jolly self, and entertain them with amusing stories; but his spirit was as if paralyzed. He knew the brother-in-law was right, and therefore felt no resentment, though it was such a crushing blow to his pride not to be able to complete a work begun.

On the way home strange, gloomy thoughts arose in him; he wondered if he were not one whose every undertaking was doomed to failure. There was a time when he thought himself a veritable Fortune's Favourite. That was when he had captured his wife and taken over Mårbacka. But later on he had had a lot of ill-luck. For one thing, he had asked for his discharge from the military service merely because of a slight reprimand from his captain. He had been overhasty, but he did not worry about that. What did rankle in him, though, was that he had not been appointed Paymaster of the Regiment, to succeed his father. The office had been abolished, and the duties pertaining to it had been divided between four muster-clerks, of whom he was one. But the work was unimportant and the remuneration small. Then there was the attempt to have the river dredged—it. too, had failed.

Midway between Gårdsjö and Mårbacka lies As
Springs, an old health resort he had once undertaken
to modernize. He had built a fine new bath house and
engaged a corps of male and female attendants, with
the hope that health-seekers would flock to the place.
That was also a failure. Now and again an invalid
came, but it hardly paid to keep the resort open.

And to cap it all, his barn-building was a lamentable
failure! There must be something lacking in him, he
thought; he was perhaps less capable than other men.
The best thing he could do was to give up his plans,
settle down in his rocker, read his newspaper, and let
things run on in the old ruts.

Coming home he found his wife seated on the front
steps awaiting him. She was very like her brother at
Gårdsjö; she had the same intelligent face, the same
clear head, the same serious turn of mind, the same love
of work and indifference to pleasure, and the same dis-
like of all that was uncertain and venturesome.

The Lieutenant was very fond of his wife and moreover respected her judgment as he did her brother's.
But that evening he would rather she had not sat up
for him. She, too, was against him in this building
project.

"What did Kalle say?" Fru Lagerlöf asked him, as
they went to their room.

"He thinks like you and the rest, that I should give
up the work."

Fru Lagerlöf made no reply. She had dropped into

her usual place, by the sewing table, and sat looking out into the light summer night, with no thought, apparently, of retiring.

The Lieutenant had already flung off his coat. "Aren't you going to bed?" he asked. His rasping tones betrayed his irritation and despondency.

"I think," said the wife in a low, even voice—still gazing into the night—"I think you should finish it."

"What are you saying?" the Lieutenant queried impatiently. He had heard what she said, but thought he must have misunderstood.

"I think," she repeated, "that you ought to go on with it."

"Is it the barn you're speaking of?" he asked, going up to her. Her words had awakened a little hope in him, yet he was not certain that he had understood her aright.

Fru Lagerlöf had been turning this matter over in her mind the whole evening; she had said to herself that it would not be well for her husband to go short in yet another undertaking. It might be more expedient perhaps to give over the building scheme; but that would go too hard with him. This was something which her father or her brother could not understand; but she—his wife—understood.

To read the hearts of those she loved—that was as easy to Fru Lagerlöf as reading a book; but to put her own thoughts into words in a moment of deep feeling she could no more do than she could interpret Hebrew.

"I don't think as Kalle does," she said.

"What are you talking about?" The Lieutenant was almost trembling with suspense. He dared not believe even now that she had come to his way of thinking.

Seeing how agitated he was, she did her utmost to make him understand.

"I don't agree with Kalle," she said. "I think you should finish building the barn, and that it should stand where you want to have it. And I think we ought to put a mortgage on the estate so that we can get along without having to ask Father for more money."

Now at last the Lieutenant understood. A great light broke in upon him. If the wife and he were of one mind there were no difficulties ahead. The foundation was solid and the walls rose firmly.

"God bless you, Louise!" he said.

After that they seemed to be more closely drawn to each other than ever, held by new bonds of sympathy and tenderness. And the wife was consulted at every step in the building work.

When at last the doors of the new barn were thrown open, and the cows were ceremoniously led in and tied to their cribs; when the chickens and geese, the turkeys and ducks were driven into their cages and the calves into the stalls; when light streamed in through the large windows and they themselves walked in clean, smooth passageways, they felt that a good work had been done, and were glad they had both had a share in it.

III

THE GARDEN

MAMSELLE LOVISA certainly loved and admired her brother the Lieutenant, but she did not see why he need introduce so many changes and newfangled things. She thought Mårbacka might better be left as it was in their parents' time. What went against her most was his wanting to lay out gardens on all sides of the dwelling house.

She had been quite worried when he talked of deepening the river-bed, and felt relieved when his plan miscarried. It was such a pretty sight, when Ämtan overflowed and formed a lot of little shimmering lakes down in the meadows! And she wailed a good deal when her brother cleared away the field flowers. It had been a veritable feast for the eyes when one field was white with daisies, another violet with heart's-ease, and a third yellow with buttercups. And it was a great pity the cows were no longer sent to pasture in the woods. Everybody knew that such thick cream and such yellow butter as one got when they wandered in the forest were never seen when they grazed in the meadow.

In her father's time, and for hundreds of years before, it had been the custom to cut down the saplings, leave them on the ground to dry, then burn them where they lay. The following year the ashes were sown with rye, and, later, these burn-beaten clearings were covered with wild strawberries and raspberries. Mamselle Lovisa naturally took it to heart when her brother no longer burned such "falls."

"Mark my words," she said to him, "there'll soon be an end to the wild berries. Where will they grow if the woods are not burn-beaten? If all were to do as you are doing, we'd never again be able to sit of a summer's evening and watch the pretty fires round the wooded hills."

And she was not pleased with the new barn, either. Of course she did not know very much, she said, but she had been told there was never any comfort in a stone barn.

When the new barn was finished and the old one torn down, and the Lieutenant talked of laying out a new garden, Mamselle Lovisa was beside herself.

"I trust you know what you're about," she said. "A large garden requires constant care, so you will have to figure on keeping a gardener. Unless a garden is properly tended and kept clear of weeds, one might better have none at all."

The Lieutenant let her admonitions go into one ear and out of the other. In the autumn he began tearing down the fences, which had been there since Pastor Wennervik's time—those enclosing the kitchen garden and rose garden and those surrounding the front and back yards.

"Well, this is the end of all comfort and joy in this place!" sighed Mamselle Lovisa. "Think how secure one felt when once inside all the white fences! And what fun it was for the children to run out and open the gates when company came!"

"It was less fun, though, for the one who had to keep so many fences and gates in repair," the Lieutenant replied.

He went right on with his work. When the fences were down he ploughed up the old kitchen garden and the little rose garden, the old trampled sward, the ground where the old barn had stood, and the calf ward, so as to have the grounds cleared for the laying of the garden in the spring.

"Is it true that you're going to remove the kitchen garden?" said Mamselle Lovisa. "To be sure I don't know anything, but I have heard folks say that when the apple trees are allowed to grow in the herb beds they bear well, but if one plants sod round them one can't expect much fruit."

"But dear little Lovisa, I thought you would be glad to have a real garden!"

"Glad! Should I be glad that you are destroying the old Mårbacka? Soon we won't know the place at all."

The Lieutenant thought his sister unusually contentious in this instance, which was the more surprising because she had always loved flowers and cared for all the house plants. But at that time, which was shortly after her engagement had been broken and she was still suffering from the disappointment, he could not say a harsh word to her. All day long she paced the floor of her room and he could hear her restless steps when he sat in the living room reading. He understood that she was not just then quite mistress of herself, and thought it a favourable sign that she took an interest in something outside her own unhappiness. It was better that she should disapprove of his garden than be continually brooding on whether she had been too hasty in sending back the betrothal ring, or whether her fiancé had turned against her because she had put a few leaves of whortleberry in Kaisa Nilsdotter's bridal-crown.

In those days there was an old landscape gardener living in Fryksdalen who in his prime had been head gardener on various large estates. He had the name of being a veritable wizard at garden making, and when anyone contemplated laying out a new garden his advice and assistance were sought.

The Lieutenant had asked him to come to Mårbacka, and in the spring, as soon as the frost was out of the ground, the old man appeared with his drawings and prints. A large corps of workmen was placed at his command; quantities of bushes and trees ordered from the Göteborg nurseries had come, and the big work was now started.

When the ground had been levelled the gardener and the Lieutenant went about all day staking out grass plots and gravel walks. The old man informed the Lieutenant that it was no longer the custom to follow the severely regular French style. Now the paths must all be winding and the borders and flower beds in easy, graceful lines. What he had in mind for Mårbacka he called the English style; but the Lieutenant rather suspected that the style was the old man's own and not of foreign origin.

In front they laid out a big circular lawn, on one side of which they set out shrubbery in the shape of an egg, and on the other shrubbery in the form of a horn of plenty, while in the middle of the round they planted a weeping ash. Up toward the veranda they staked out a star-shaped flower bed, placing as a guard about it four provence-rose bushes—each on its own little round spot.

On the old sand-plot just below the kitchen windows they staked out a large triangle and filled it with rich soil, in which they transplanted the rose bushes from the old rose garden. For of roses they could never have enough. Along the front of the house they set out a low hedge of primroses, and two white-brier-rose bushes were given the places of honour, the one before the parlour window, the other before the front bedroom window.

The Lieutenant took such keen delight in this work that he went about with the gardener all day, and Fru

Lagerlöf would snatch long moments from her sewing
to go out and have a look at the garden; but Mamselle
Lovisa persistently kept to her room. This delightful
spring work only tended to increase her sadness. She
would rather have had the old trampled sward, with its
one little tangle of snowberry bushes. All these innova-
tions seemed to her so unnecessary. But what she
thought or said was immaterial; just the same, folk
had managed to live at Mårbacka before. All these
modern improvements only meant a lot of bother and
needless expense.

But the work went on despite her disapproval. Round
the stable the gardener planted a hedge of lilacs, also
on three sides of the dwelling house, while along the
wing he set out a hedge of spiræas. That done, the
Lieutenant and the gardener went at the old Wennervik
kitchen garden. The fine apple trees they let stand
where they were, but the ground about them was laid
out in the old man's "English" style, with winding
gravel paths and grass plots arranged in various designs.
With much skill and calculation each grass plot was
embellished with round, oblong, or triangular beds
and planted with perennials. Yellow cowslips bordered
blue iris, orange crown-imperials edged purple hyssop,
and encircling the red carnations was a wreath of
pink bellis.

The flower beds of course were up round the dwelling
house. Farther back, on both the north and south
sides, place was made for gooseberry and currant

bushes, for strawberry patches, for plum trees, pear trees, and ever so many cherry trees. At the far southern end, quite a distance away and well out of sight, lay the new kitchen garden, while at the north end was a little birch grove, bordered by mountain ash and bird-cherry trees. This grove the gardener included in his design, in order to create at least the suggestion of a park. He intersected the grove with many narrow winding gravel walks. In three places he cleared away the trees to make room for tables and seats. The first open space was an oblong spot with settees on all sides. Here the lady of the house was to receive her guests, and it was to be called the Tea Corner. The second was a square, with four seats round a table. That was for the master and his company, and the old man jokingly dubbed it the Toddy Corner. The third space had only a long, narrow bench. That was the children's domain, and was to be known as the Kiddies' Corner.

But all this planting left Mamselle Lovisa indifferent. It may almost be said that she scorned and detested it. She had not yet set foot in the new garden.

Soon pale-green sprouts sprang up in the sod, the newly planted bushes sent forth tender, shy little leaves, the perennial plants pushed through the soil of the garden beds; oaks, chestnuts, and Lombardy poplars, which had been planted in the old barn lot, began to bud and show that they were alive.

In the midst of this busy time an unexpected difficulty arose. The old gardener was obliged to go home for a few days, to see to his own garden. That would not have mattered much but for the hot-bed he had made in order to coax up some asters and gilly-flowers for the beds in the front yard.

"Who is going to tend the hot-bed while I'm away?" said the old gardener. "You know, Lieutenant, a hot-bed needs constant watching."

"I'll do it myself," the Lieutenant replied; for by that time he thought himself almost a master gardener. He let the old man show him how to air and water the plants.

The morning the gardener left there was bright, strong sunshine. Along in the forenoon the Lieutenant in alarm went up to the house to find his wife. As she was nowhere about he rushed into his sister's room.

"You'll have to come and help me with the hot-bed, Lovisa," he said. Then, remembering that Mamselle Lovisa would not even look at his garden and took no interest whatever in his work, he thought: "Oh, well, it's said now, and she can't do more than refuse."

But instead she eagerly got up and went out with him. Instantly she saw the little plants, which were wilted and drooping, she exclaimed:

"The sun is too strong on them, they must be shaded." Then she found something with which to protect them, and the plants were saved.

The next day the Lieutenant had to attend a school examination. When well on his way he suddenly remembered the hot-bed. There was the same scorching heat that day as on the previous one. Now the little plants would surely be burnt up, he thought.

The moment he got home he hurried over to the hot-bed. To his surprise and delight all was well; the plants stood up, erect and sturdy. His sister had thought of the poor little things which he had neglected. He promptly decided not to forget to water and close the hot-bed that evening. Sometime after supper he sprang up in alarm.

"Why, I'm forgetting the hot-bed! It should have been closed this long while."

Mamselle Lovisa said nothing, but let him go see for himself. He found the glass lids down and the covers spread over them.

The following day the Lieutenant did not look at the hot-bed or give it a thought. All the same, the little plants fared well. Mamselle Lovisa weeded and loosened the soil round them, watered and tended them in every way. It seemed rather strange that only she should think of the hot-bed; but for her everything sown there would have died. Of course she wished the old gardener would return and relieve her of the work; but while he was away she had to go on with it.

He was gone longer than expected. In the meantime the plants were growing almost too large for trans-planting. There was no other course than for Mamselle Lovisa to set them out in the flower beds herself. When that much had been done, what could she do but go on weeding and watering them all summer, until the gilly, petunia, aster, and snap-dragon plants were in bloom!

And when the perfectly formed star before the front steps at Mårbacka appeared resplendent with bright colours, then in some mysterious way the pain was gone from Mamselle Lovisa's wounded heart. The little plants had requited the loving care she had bestowed upon them. They had given her a new interest in life, a new field of activity.

Lieutenant Lagerlöf did not have to engage a head gardener for Mårbacka; Mamselle Lovisa had inherited the old Wennervik bent, and it was she who took care of the garden. The flowers were her faithful friends; they loved her as she loved them. People wondered how she could get them to bloom and glow as in no other garden. They did not know that the flowers had caught colour and sweetness from her vanished dream of happiness.

IV

THE ROOF TRUSSES

WHEN Lieutenant Lagerlöf and his little daughters walked in the garden or out in the fields they often talked of what they would do if the King came to Mårbacka.

In those days the King used to drive through Värmland several times a year on his way to and from Norway, and he had to stop somewhere for refreshment and rest. Most frequently he stayed over in Karlstad, at the Governor's house, and it was also his wont to honour with a royal visit the great manors which lay along his route, and where they could conveniently entertain him.

Of course there was not the least likelihood that the King would come to a little unknown place like Mårbacka, which, to boot, lay far from the great highway. But that did not trouble the Lieutenant and his little girls. It would not have been such fun perhaps to talk about this had there been any chance of the King's really coming. Now it was only a pleasure to build in fancy a triumphal arch for His Majesty, and strew flowers in his way as he drove up. The little girls wondered if they should dress in white when the King came and the Lieutenant generously promised them new white frocks made by the best sempstress in East Ämtervik for the grand occasion.

The Lieutenant and the children pictured to themselves how the King, when nearing Mårbacka, would suddenly shade his eyes with his hand so as to see better.

"What is that great white building over there in the meadow?" he would ask. "Have they two churches in this parish?"

"No, your Majesty," the Lieutenant would then reply (for of course he was to ride with the King), "that white building is not a church, it is my cow-barn."

Then the King would look at him in wide-eyed wonder, and say:

"By Jove! You must be a deucedly clever fellow, Eric Gustaf, to have built yourself a barn like that!"

How they were to house the King and all his retinue in the little one-story dwelling—that was an almost unsolvable problem. The Lieutenant had often talked of building another story, and they were all agreed that when that was finished it would be an easy matter to entertain the King. Even then they probably would be a bit cramped for space. The Lieutenant and his wife might have to spend the night in the hay-loft, and the children—well, they could sleep in the rabbit hutch.

Now that about the rabbit hutch tickled the little girls immensely. And they wondered what the King would say about the garden. Of course he would marvel to find away back here in the farming country a garden laid out in the true English manner. At that, the Lieutenant would immediately send word to the old gardener and hearten him with the good news that the King had praised his flower beds and gravel paths.

And then when the King was leaving Mårbacka he would present Fru Lagerlöf with a gold brooch and Mamselle Lovisa with a gold bracelet, and the old house-keeper would receive a large shawl-pin of silver. Before stepping into his carriage, His Majesty would shake hands with the Lieutenant, and say:

"Thanks and honour to you, Eric Gustaf Lagerlöf! It is but a modest bit of my realm that is in your keeping, but I see that you take good care of it."

Those words the Lieutenant would remember with joy as long as he lived. He and his children had right merry times on these little excursions into the land of make-believe. It was a pity, though, that the royal visit could not really and truly come about until the Lieutenant had built a second story.

Then, lo and behold, at the close of the eighteen-sixties, when the Lieutenant had finished with everything else, he was ready to start remodelling the house. The royal visit apart, they were rather closely housed in the old one-story dwelling. The Lieutenant had already made some alterations. Eight or ten years back he had cut out larger window openings and had done away with the small-paned sashes. He had also put up new tile-stoves, papered the walls of the parlour and living room, and built a large veranda in place of the old porch.

Now there were to be still further improvements. The whole roof was to be torn off, the trusses raised, and the timber walls heightened. The year before he had had a couple of good carpenters at work on the place preparing the new roof trusses, so that the roof could be raised and covered as quickly as possible. The workmen had but just finished the trusses when the Lieutenant got word that his father-in-law had passed away. This was a sad loss and a heavy blow as well. The Lieutenant had lost his main prop and stay. Hereafter he would have no one but himself to depend on. Now out of his estate he must pay all contracted debts. His sons were then nearly grown and must soon be sent to the University of Upsala; therefore he thought it best to postpone the building work for a year or so.

But what one puts off is likely to be left undone. Fresh obstacles continually loomed in the way of this work. One year the Lieutenant was ill, and the next he had to help a brother-in-law who had once been well-to-do but must now have a yearly stipend. While the Lieutenant had been labouring to build up his property the years had passed without his noting them. He was now a man of fifty, and the old daring spirit of enterprise had perhaps slipped away from him.

It was with no light heart he relinquished his cherished plan of rebuilding the house. That was to have been his crowning work.   All his life he had dreamed of erecting a fine manor-house on his beloved Mårbacka.

The great piles of timber and the finished roof trusses lay in the backyard for many years.   Whenever the Lieutenant walked past them he turned his head away; he could not bear to look at them.   His little daughters had been so very happy when he started on the roof trusses, and not altogether on account of the "royal visit."   It was perhaps of more importance to them that they should have a real salon to dance in, and that the house should have two stories, and be as grand as Iron-Master Wallroth's Gårdsjö or Engineer Noreen's country seat.   They grew uneasy over the delay, year after year, and one of the girls finally mustered the courage to ask her father when he was going to put up those roof trusses.

"I'm afraid never, my child!"   When he said this his face twitched and there was a strange catch in his voice.   Then, quickly recovering himself, he added, banteringly:

"But it doesn't matter now, my girl.   They are building a railway to Norway, and hereafter the King won't come asking for a night's lodging, either at Mårbacka or any other manor in Värmland."

WORKDAYS AND FÊTE-DAYS

I

LIEUTENANT LAGERLÖF believed that children, in order to grow up healthy and strong and become useful and capable men and women, should above all things acquire the habit of nooning. With that object in mind, always, after the midday meal, he would take the two youngest children down to the farm-office, which was in another building a few steps from the house.

The office was a large room, and probably looked about the same as in the days of the Mårbacka clergymen, when it had been their study. At the far end, under a window, there was a black leather lounge, and before it an oblong table. Along one side-wall stood a bedstead, a black leather-seated chair, a large black walnut writing table, and a high chest of drawers, while at the other side stood another bed and black leather chair and a tile stove. On the wall, beyond the stove, hung three fowling pieces, a seal-skin game-bag, a large horse-pistol, a couple of powder horns, and a fencing foil which crossed a broken sabre. In the midst of this armoury rested a huge pair of elk antlers. Down by the door, on one side, there was a stationary clothes cupboard, on the other side, a bookcase. At the bottom of the cupboard reposed the Lieutenant's iron-bound oak chest, the one the Paymaster of the Regiment had used, and which was a bit charred on one corner.

In the bookcase the Lieutenant kept his big ledgers, and there, also, were the school books of two generations. Many annuals of the *European Feuilleton* were crowded in with Homer, Cicero, and Livy. Histories of Peter the Great and Frederick the Wise had been relegated hither on account of their common drab cardboard bindings, also the works of Wilhelm von Braun—though not because of their covers but for other reasons. On the floor lay surveyors' instruments from the time the Lieutenant had assisted in the shifting of boundary lines; also some boxes of fishing tackle and odds and ends.

First thing, on coming into the office, the Lieutenant and his little daughters had to drive out the flies. Doors and windows were thrown wide open. The Lieutenant caught up a towel for the chase, and the little girls took off their aprons and went to beating the air. They climbed on to chairs and tables, hunted and swatted, while the buzzing flies flew hither and yon, as if determined not to go. However, in the end they were cleared out, and windows and doors were closed.

But there was one fly they called the Old Office Fly; she was used to the daily chase, and knew enough to keep out of the way while it went on. When all was quiet and peaceful again, she would come forth from her hiding place and seat herself on the ceiling.

No fresh chase was started for her. The Lieutenant and the children knew that she was too canny for them. They could never get rid of her! So they went on to the next thing to be done before nooning. The girls arranged two leather pillows and a down pillow on the lounge as a head-rest for the Lieutenant; whereupon he stretched himself out, shut his eyes, and simulated sleep.

Then, with wild shrieks, the children threw themselves upon him. He tossed them off as if they were little balls of yarn, but back they came like playful puppies. They pulled his whiskers, ruffled his hair, and clambered up on to the sofa, playing all sorts of pranks on him.

When the Lieutenant thought the children had had enough of play he clapped his hands once, and said:

"It's over now."

Little good that did! The children kept right on; again and again they crawled up on to the sofa, were flung off, and came bounding back—shrieking and making a fearful racket.

When that had gone on for some little time, the Lieutenant clapped twice and said: "It's quite over now."

Nor did that have any effect. The same performance was repeated amid shrieks and laughter, until the Lieutenant presently clapped his hands three times, and said:

"Now it is really and truly over."

The two children instantly hushed their noise, and each crept into her own bed to sleep.

After a little the Lieutenant began to snore. His snores were not very loud, but they were enough to keep the two children, who were to acquire the habit of nooning, awake.

The youngsters were not allowed to get out of bed or speak to each other, but had to lie perfectly still. Their eyes, meanwhile, wandered round the room. Gazing at the rag mats on the floor, they recognized their mother's and their aunt's old dresses, which had been cut up for carpets. They looked at the portrait of General Malmberg, which hung on the wall between two battle canvasses, at the ink-well and pen, at the antlers and game-bags, at the foil and the famous gun called the "harekiller." They traced the figures in the quilt, they counted the stars on the wall-paper, the nail-heads along the floor, and the checks in the curtains. The hour seemed dreadfully long! They heard the merry voices of the other children, who were so big they did not have to take a midday nap, but ran about—happy and free—devouring cherries and goose-berries and green apples!

The sole hope of the two little girls was the "office fly." She buzzed and buzzed round the Lieutenant's face, making as much noise as she could. If only she kept at it long enough she'd wake him up!

II

THE undergraduates at the *Gymnasium* of Karlstad had been unusually quiet in the beginning of the autumn semester. They had not started any fights with the street boys, or been up to any other deviltry. The whole city was surprised, pleased, and thankful, though no doubt people felt at the same time that something was lacking.

Then, as it drew on toward autumn Fair-time, when folk from all parts of Värmland were coming to the capital of the province, the students felt they must do something to maintain their reputation. Now it was not merely a question of Karlstad, but of all Värmland. After due deliberation, when various propositions had been presented and rejected, a schoolboy named Fredrik Sandberg was summoned to appear before the collegians.

Fredrik Sandberg obeyed orders, of course, for in those days it never would have done for the schoolboys to defy the collegians, who were their overlords. Nor would it have been well for the one who attempted to evade a summons from that quarter!

When Fredrik came the students togged him out

in frilled shirt and stock, satin waistcoat of large
flowered pattern, gray trousers with foot-straps, blue
swallow-tail coat with silver buttons, and patent
leather shoes. His hair was then curled and arranged
in a forelock, gloves and walking stick were put into
his hands, and a tall stove-pipe hat with curved brim
topped it all.

If only Fredrik Sandberg had not been so small that
the trousers hung in pleats, the coat tails almost trailed
on the ground, and the hat went down on his ears, he
would have been as fine a dandy as ever trod a city
street. Thus arrayed, he was ordered off to Mamselle
Brorström's.

When Fredrik Sandberg entered the attic room where
Mamselle Brorström lived, he found her standing before her tile-stove making waffles. Her attire was a
bit so-so—just a petticoat and undervest. The little
schoolboy thought to himself that never had he seen
such arms and legs, such hands and feet, and such a
torso!

"My name is Fredrik Sandberg," he said by way of
introduction, "and I would most humbly beg that I
may be permitted to invite Mamselle Brorström to the
Fair Ball at the Masonic Lodge."

Mamselle Brorström was not exactly what would be
termed "in society," and had surely never thought of
going to a fair ball. But now, being invited by an
elegant cavalier, she could hardly refuse. So, curtsy-
ing to Fredrik Sandberg, she thanked him and said she

felt highly honoured, and would be most happy to attend the ball.

The boy was pleased at being so well received, for it might have turned out quite otherwise. He ran back to the students as quickly as possible, and reported all that had taken place.

A week later Fredrik Sandberg was again ordered to appear before the collegians, and again dressed up as before, and sent to Mamselle Brorström.

This time he found her standing before her looking-glass trying on a red tulle dress. Her neck and arms were bare and she turned and twisted impatiently, apparently in a dreadful humour.

The little boy stared at the huge woman, who was twice as tall as he, twice as broad, and twice as strong. He gazed at the thick arms sticking out from the sleeve-less red tulle bodice, and the enormous legs showing below the short skirts; he looked at her coarse face, copper-coloured from constant exposure to fire—for she was always making waffles—and he looked at her black tousled hair standing out like a bush round her head; he saw the fiery gleam in her blood-shot eyes and heard the thundering tones of her raucous voice. The boy wanted to cut and run, but having been sent there by the college students and knowing what disobedience to that authority meant, he bowed to Mamselle Brorström, and said:

"I most humbly beg that I may have the pleasure of the first waltz at the Fair Ball."

Mamselle Brorström had been rather repentant and thoughtful that morning, and had wondered if she really ought to go to the ball. She would no doubt have put all thought of it out of her mind if Fredrik Sandberg had not come and begged for the first waltz. But now that she was certain of a dancing partner she was again in good humour. She assured Fredrik Sandberg that she felt both favoured and honoured, and that nothing would afford her greater pleasure than to let him dance with her.

That was the very day of the ball. And in the evening Mamselle Brorström, arrayed in her red tulle dress (than which nothing could be prettier, she thought) appeared at the Masonic Lodge among Karlstaders and Fair visitors. Stalking through the ladies' dressing room into the grand ballroom, she sat herself down on one of the small cushioned seats along the wall.

People stared, but she did not mind. Having been invited, she had as good a right as any one else to dance at the Fair Ball. She noticed that the other ladies all had acquaintances to chat with, but this did not trouble her; when once the music struck up for the dance, they'd see that she had as fine a partner as any of them.

The regiment band began to play. She saw the foundry clerks step up to the founderers' daughters, the lieutenants to the officers' ladies, and the shop clerks to the shopkeepers' girls—each took his partner. Soon everyone was on the floor whirling round—everyone except Mamselle Brorström, who sat waiting for Fredrik Sandberg.

The collegians were on the platform with the musicians. They had a good view of Mamselle Brorström in her red tulle, sitting all alone in the middle of the long row of wall seats, where the one she was waiting for might easily find her.

The wife of the Governor put up her lorgnette and wondered who that large, conspicuous looking woman was. The daughters of the founderers stuck up their noses at her, while the young ladies of the nobility marvelled that a person of that sort should come to a Fair Ball.

Mamselle Brorström meanwhile remained seated in the one place. Fredrik Sandberg did not put in an appearance and no one else seemed to think of asking her to dance. There was a supper, and after that more dancing. The fine folk were now leaving and the gentlemen began to look a bit flushed; but Mamselle Brorström still sat on.

Then at last Tanner Grunder stepped up and asked for a polka.

" 'Tis high time!" said Mamselle Brorström in a voice loud enough to be heard all over the ballroom. And those words became a catch phrase in Värmland.

The tanner had been in a side room playing cards the whole evening, and had just come out for a little spin. As she was the only lady disengaged he naturally went over to her—not knowing, of course, her state of mind.

As Mamselle Brorström stood up to fling herself into the dizzy whirl, Tanner Grunder, to be polite and obliging, said:

"What is Mamselle Brorström's pleasure—to dance forward or backward?"

" 'Tis all one to me just so it goes," she answered.

This, too, was heard all over the hall, and those words also became a saying in Värmland.

The day after the ball Fredrik Sandberg was again summoned by the collegians, and once again he was togged out and sent to Mamselle Brorström.

He found her standing by the stove, as usual, making waffles. That day she was not attired in red tulle but only in her petticoat and undervest. The schoolboy thought that never had he seen such a sourlooking face, such strong arms and formidable fists. The words he was to speak wanted to stick in his throat. But just outside the door stood three of the most dangerous collegians, and Fredrik knew what it would mean to get into the bad graces of the powers that be!

"I most humbly beg to know whether Mamselle Brorström had a pleasant time last evening at the ball," he said, and made a low bow.

How Fredrik Sandberg got out of the room, across the hall, down the stairs, and into the street, he never knew. Nor did the three collegians who had been lurking behind the door know how they had been assisted down the stairs. It was well they were there, so that

Fredrik was not alone on this treat, which proved to be more than enough for them all.

This episode was imprinted indelibly in the mind of Lieutenant Lagerlöf, who at the time it occurred was a lad attending school at Karlstad. And of an evening, as he sat in his rocker, he would tell the tale to his children. Though he was himself the kindest and gentlest of men, the mad pranks of schoolboys were always a source of amusement to him.

III

IN Grandmother Lagerlöf's time, when the paupers of the community were taken into families and cared for, there was an old wardswoman at Mårbacka who on winter nights used to sleep in the kitchen —though goodness knows the room was crowded enough anyhow, with the housekeeper and five maids all sleeping there! So at the first signs of summer she would betake herself to the barn-loft, where she had found a good comfortable bed in an old discarded sledge, which in bygone winters had been used for carting pig-iron from the smithies in Bergslagerna to the Kymsberg Iron Works.

There for several weeks she had slept in peace and quiet. Then, one night, she was awakened by the sledge moving. She sat bolt upright and looked round. Outside, the night was almost as light as day, but in the barn where the poor old woman lay it was pitch dark, so that she could not see anything. Thinking that she had only been dreaming, she sank back upon her pillow and was soon slumbering again.

But strange to say, she had no more than got to sleep when the sledge began to move again. This time it

not only gave a little lurch but went gliding along
the floor. Though it moved kind of slowly and cautiously, there was no mistaking that there was life in it.

The old woman sat up and gripped the side of the
sledge with both hands. Her hair rose and her jaw
fell.

"Merciful God!" she gasped, "it's crawling!"

But how in the world could such a thing happen?
Could it be that an old sledge which had carried pig-
iron winter after winter between Bergslagerna and
Kymsberg grew restless at night, and must bestir itself
a bit once in a while?

The sledge moved faster; now it went bumpety-
bump over the uneven floor, and scudded across piles
of hay and straw as if taking plunges into deep gulches
and flights up steep hills.

"O merciful God! Merciful God!" cried the woman.

But invoking the name of the Lord did not stop the
sledge; it ran right on the whole length of the barn-
loft, till it struck the wall.

There it must surely stand still, she thought. But no
indeed! As soon as it recovered its breath, so to speak,
it began to back toward the corner where it first stood.

The wardswoman said later that if in that instant she
had not guessed what was wrong with the sledge she
surely would have lost her wits.

Oh, no, it was not the old Bergslag journeys haunting
the pig-iron sledge—someone had "greased" it! Some
witch-hag on the farm or in the district (she didn't

care to mention any names, or even think them) had taken it into her head that she could ride to Blåkulla, the Witches'-kitchen, with more ease and comfort in the old sledge than on a broom-stick, an oven-rake, or a barn door. Perhaps the wicked witch did not know the wardswoman slept in the sledge. In the stress of the moment there was no time to figure on just how it had all come about. But this much was certain: the sledge wanted to be out and off, and it was she— the wardswoman—it was taking to the Witches' hell instead of the right one.

Lord o' Mercy! But for the strong barn wall she would already be flying over the village toward the church.

Meanwhile the sledge kept backing. She knew well enough that that was only in order to make a fresh start to break through. Once outside, it would go shooting through the air over tree-tops and mountain ranges. She would be flying above shining lakes and rivers, without the least fear of tumbling into them; she would circle round the church steeple like a jackdaw, and fly on beyond Stor Kil and Grav parishes; but where she would land she hated to think on.

Lord o' Mercy! The sledge was rushing forward again. There was no doubt that sledge could fly if once it got out into the open; it was making for the wall at terrific speed. The old woman, positive now that the wall would give way, lay down again so as not to be scraped off in the middle when the sledge cut through the boards.

This time it struck hard. Oh, what a bump! Again
the wall resisted. Now, if only the sledge had the
sense to see that it couldn't get anywhere, and stand
still!

But don't for a moment imagine it! Once more it
began to back. That sledge must have been greased
with real witch-oil. If it made a third attempt it would
surely succeed. Whatever would she do when she got
in amongst witches and all the Hosts of Darkness!
To be sure she had heard tell of such, but she had
never wanted to believe in them. There is so much
one would rather not believe until one has seen for
oneself whether it is true.

"Merciful Lord, lead me not into temptation," she
prayed. All her life she had endured poverty and con-
tempt without a murmur. But were she now to be
offered riches and power, would she be able to resist?
Or, were she to learn the magic words that cure sickness in humans and animals, or the ones that make
the ground yield good harvests, or those that awaken
love in young folk, could she withstand the temptation
to use them? Might she only be granted strength to
rise above temptation and so preserve her soul unto
salvation.

Just then the sledge took a third lunge. Now it tore
ahead, creating a rush of wind that whizzed about her
ears. She shut her eyes lest she turn giddy, for in
the wink of an eyelid she knew she would be soaring
high above the earth—high as the lark.

Crash! Now, surely, the wall had given way. . . .

But, thanks be to God! the good board wall still held; it was only the sledge that had broken down. With that, it must have lost all zest for travel. The sledge having come to a dead stop, the wardswoman managed to crawl out and drop down on a heap of straw, to rest after her perilous ride. When in the morning she told it all to the maids and it eventually came to the ears of Grandmother Lagerlöf, the latter thought it sounded a bit queer. Though Grandmother was herself a firm believer in the supernatural, there had to be some semblance of reason and probability behind it. That one could ride to *Blåkulla* on a light summer's night, and in a sleigh at that, was something unheard of. Grandmother, of course, went down to the barn and examined the sledge. Finding a couple of long ropes attached to it, she immediately summoned the stableboy and two or three of his companions. After questioning the boys thoroughly, she gave them a good dressing down.

This, too, was one of the Lieutenant's boy-prank yarns. There were many more up his sleeve; but when he had told this and the one about Mamselle Brorström, Fru Lagerlöf would say:

"Now that is enough for this evening. It's time for the children to say Good-night, and go to bed."

IV

AT SIX-THIRTY every morning Nurse made a fire in the children's room, and at seven o'clock the children had to rise and start dressing. When they were ready, say at about half after seven, and the beds had been hurriedly made, a tray was sent up from the kitchen with bowls of gruel and large pieces of buttered *knäckebröd*. This was the *little* breakfast. Then, until eight, they sat at a large table by the window and glanced over their lessons. The nursery had to serve as schoolroom, there being no other place available.

On the stroke of eight books were closed. The children then put on their wraps and went out in the half-dark winter morning—whatever the weather. They hurried down to the pond first thing, to see whether there was ice for skating, or, in lieu of that, went sledding on the driveway. If there was nothing else they could do, they ran down to the barn to see the baby rabbits and romp with the sheep-dog.

A little before nine they had *big* breakfast, which usually consisted of eggs, or griddle-cakes, or fried herring with boiled potatoes, or black pudding with

salt pork and cream gravy. At breakfast the family
did not sit at the big table, but each person, in turn,
helped himself and then sat down at one of the side
tables.

At nine sharp one had to be through with the meal,
for at that hour lessons began. Then it was back to
the nursery again to sit at the long table reading,
writing, and figuring until noon. The little girls had a
governess now—Ida Melanoz, eldest daughter of Sexton Melanoz, who had her father's good brain and
teaching ability.

At twelve o'clock dinner was served at the round
dining table. One of the little girls said grace before
the meal, the other after it. Then, rising from table,
they kissed Mother's hand and Father's hand, and
said: "Thanks for the food." It was never quiet during the dinner hour. Lieutenant Lagerlöf kept the
ball of chatter rolling. He could always find something
to talk about. If nothing more thrilling had happened
than his meeting an old woman in the lane, he would
make a whole story out of the incident.

From one to two the children were again out of doors.
But they often went in a few minutes before the play
hour was up, so as to run through their lessons for the
afternoon session, which was from two to four. Afterwards, they would read the lessons for the next day.
They were never allowed to sit at their studies later
than five o'clock, when they must go out-doors again.
Now they were off to some distant coasting hill. At

one time they had a big ram to drive, and that, of course, was great sport. When they got back to the house a pleasant hour awaited them. A log fire crackled in the living room and on the folded card table stood a plate of sandwiches and a pitcher of un-fermented beer. To sit or lie before the fire while munching their sandwiches—that was something the youngsters enjoyed hugely. They chattered and plan-ned all sorts of things. It was the only hour of the day they had to themselves.

When the fire burned low, the lamp on the round table over by the sofa was lit. Fru Lagerlöf now took her little daughters in hand, and taught them to sew, crochet, and knit. She had a volume of Hans Ander-sen's fairy tales, and when she thought the work had gone well she would reward the children by reading or narrating "The Travelling Companion," or "The Tinder-box," or "The Wild Swans." Besides, there were pretty and amusing illustrations in that book, and to look at those was almost as much fun as to hear the stories.

At eight o'clock supper was served, and then the Lieutenant appeared. Up to that hour he had been at the farm-office poring over his ledgers.

And now, after the long work-filled day, one could at last relax. The children put away their needlework, and the Lieutenant, sitting back in his rocking-chair, began to tell schoolboy yarns like the one about Mam-selle Brorström, or else he related his memories of the glorious Jenny Lind as *Norma* or the *Daughter of the Regiment,* or of Emily Högquist as the *Maid of Orleans.* When at times he did not feel like talking, he would ask Fru Lagerlöf or Mamselle Lovisa to read aloud from Tegnér. Anything more beautiful than "Fritiof's Saga" he thought had never been written. He would rather have been the Lund professor who sang of Fritiof's and Ingeborg's love, than Emperor of France or Tsar of Russia. He was also an admirer of Runeberg, whose tales of "Surgeon Stål" and epic poems he enjoyed hearing. But he did not like it if any one said the Finnish poet was greater than Tegnér.

Sometimes (and that was the best fun of all) he would sit down at the old piano and strike a few chords, then call out:

"Come, children, let's sing Bellman!"

The girls needed no coaxing, they were over by the piano in a jiffy. Then, with high glee, they let loose on Bellman! They always began with "Old Man Noah" and "Joachim of Babylon," then followed "Father Movitz" and "Mother at Tuppen," and they sang of "Dancing Master Mollberg, and His Misadventures in Rostock Tavern."

The Lieutenant pounded out the accompaniments, and hummed the air, to mark the time and carry the tune. But the children sang at the top of their voices, and could be heard all over the house. Here were indeed life and merriment for them after the day's work! They understood very little of what they sang, but the melodies put them in a glow and livened their spirits. Ah, how sweet it sounded when *Ulla* danced in spangles, veil and fringe! or when *Fredman* sang: " 'Tis as far to Monday as from north to south." And what could be funnier than when the ever-hapless *Mollberg* jumped into the vat where *Grogshop-Mother* soaked her stockfish, or when at the great boating-picnic the party-cake came on garnished with sugar, cinnamon, and anchovies!

But what delighted the children above everything was that they might sing as loud as ever they wished. The Lieutenant never corrected them or interrupted to remind them that there were such things as voice modulation and singing in unison. They thought they sang Bellman just as he should be sung.

On the wall above the piano sat Karl Mikael (Bellman) himself, with his lute. Now and then, the Lieutenant looked up at him, as if expecting a smile of approval from that incomparable lyrist and singer.

But once when Lieutenant Lagerlöf and the children were having a Bellman-sing, it happened that Colour-Sergeant von Wachenfeldt was there, sitting in his usual corner, chatting with Mamselle Lovisa.

"Isn't it strange that not one of the children has a voice?" Mamselle Lovisa remarked to the Sergeant in a half-whisper.

"Yes," replied the Sergeant in a low tone. "That they haven't singing voices they can't help, but they might at least make use of their ears!"

"It seems extraordinary, when both parents are musical, don't you think so, Wachenfeldt? I can't understand how Gustaf endures it!"

"He does not hear it as it sounds to us," said the Sergeant. "He loves those children."

"People are wont to speak of seeing with the eyes of love," observed Mamselle Lovisa, "and there may be such a thing as hearing with the ears of love. . . ."

"Be sure of that!" responded the Colour-Sergeant, who knew whereof he spoke.

One of the little singers chanced to overhear those remarks, and repeated them to the others, and perhaps it was due to that that the Bellman "concerts" at Mårbacka were suddenly discontinued.

But long afterward—aye, always—the love of the Bellman songs lived in the hearts of the Mårbacka children. They loved them not only for their humour and pathos and their haunting beauty; but the faintest tone from the Bellman lute called up memories of the never-failing love and tenderness that had made their childhood such a happy one!

V

IN THE summer of 1866 there was an unusually large number of children at Mårbacka. Besides Daniel and Johan Lagerlöf, sons of the house, there were Teodor, Otto, and Hugo Hammargren, cousins on the paternal side, who, with their parents, were spending the whole summer at Mårbacka. Ernst and Klas Schenson, cousins on the maternal side, had also come for the summer. But, indeed, they were not all! Herman, Bernhard, and Edvin Milén of the neighbouring farm, must also be counted as members of the company, and Adolf Noreen of Herrestad came over two or three times a week to play with the boys. And of course there were Anna, Selma, and Gerda Lagerlöf, though Gerda, who was only three years old, hardly counted; nor were Anna and Selma of any importance when there were so many boys around.

That summer the lads had hit upon a jollier and more satisfying pastime than any of previous years. The first few weeks they spent in the usual way—picking berries, lying on the grass, swinging in the rope-swing, shooting arrows, pitching quoits, and playing leap-frog. But after a time they wearied of these petty diversions, and talked of taking up some serious and productive work. They had an eye to a bit of woodland just beyond the avenue, which was bounded on the west by the road ditch, on the east by towering Åsberget, on the north by a stone wall, and on the south by a deep gravel pit; so that the whole area, which covered about one sixteenth of an acre, lay quite detached and well secluded.

On closer inspection, the boys discovered that the land had a bountiful supply of rocks, and its vegetation consisted mostly of juniper bushes, spruce saplings, and bracken. At the northern end there was a little brook, which ran dry in high summer, and along its shores grew some fine alder bushes. In the crevices of the mountain wall grew polypody, a kind of fern to which the boys attached great value. At the south end there were four large spruces, while in the midst of the territory stood a tall, thickly branched pine.

The whole region was evidently devoid of culture, its only inhabitants being squirrels, woodpeckers, and ants. Now the boys thought this wilderness ought to have the benefit of the blessings of civilization, and decided to emigrate and settle there.

Their first move was to stake out their homesteads. Teodor Hammargren, who was sixteen years of age and the nominal head of the expedition, claimed a towering rock, which afforded him a splendid view of the whole country. Daniel Lagerlöf, who was fifteen—and next in age and standing—appropriated the four large spruces and the fine rock wall behind them. Johan Lagerlöf and Otto Hammargren, who were schoolfellows and good pals, took joint possession of the northernmost tract with the dried-out brook and alder grove. Ernst Schenson, who was but twelve, contented himself with a scraggy rock. The others wondered what joy he could have of that. His brother, Klas, who was only a little chap, also chose a rock; but he seemed to have got the better position, for he had a shading juniper close by. Hugo Hammargren claimed as his portion the solitary pine, which no one begrudged him. Herman Milén, aged ten, found a big uprooted spruce lying with its roots in the air and its trunk full of branches. His little brothers, Bernhard and Edvin, who were twins and only eight, came near not getting anything at all; however, they were each finally allotted the stump of a tree. Adolf Noreen had not been at Mårbacka the day the land was apportioned, and there was great consternation when he finally appeared and demanded his share of the spoils; for by that time every available spot had already been taken. Luckily, Teodor Hammargren hit upon the thought of allowing him a shelf of rock in the mountain wall. And with that, peace was restored.

But if Anna and Selma had entertained any hopes of owning homes in the settlement they were sadly mistaken. Why, they were just girls, and it never even occurred to the boys that they might wish to be included.

The lads were having such good times all by themselves in their new colony! Teodor Hammargren carried up moss to his tower to make him a comfortable seat. He had built a stone stairway by which he could easily pass up and down. Daniel Lagerlöf had cleared the ground between the spruces and the rock wall, and fitted up a salon with moss-covered stone seats along three sides. His was the most comfortable and attractive place of all. Johan and Otto made for themselves a semi-circular moss sofa in among their tangle of alders. That was also considered a very desirable location. Ernst Schenson made him a wide moss-covered lounge, with his big rock as back-rest; but his brother Klas was a little do-nothing, who just sprawled on the ground under his juniper bush and didn't bother to drag stones and moss for a bench. Hugo Hammargren had begged some board-ends from the Lieutenant's carpenter and nailed them in a crotch of his pine, so that he had a grand seat. Adolf Noreen made a moss bed on his shelf of rock, where he enjoyed solid comfort when once he had clambered up. Herman Milén had dug a cave for himself under his uprooted tree, and even the small twins had spread a bit of moss over their stumps.

But Anna and Selma had nowhere to build and nothing to furnish. They wandered about the farm utterly deserted, not knowing what to do to amuse themselves.

The boys, meanwhile, had more and more fun as their commune developed. They soon found it necessary

again to play with the boys or even so much as look at
them.

"You may come up to the colony, girls, and be wait-
resses at my tavern."

Anna and Selma let the boats sail whither they would.
Not a word did they say about being forgotten and left
to shift for themselves all this long time. They went
right along with their brother to the boys' colony,
blissfully happy.

VI

IT WAS late afternoon of a beautiful day in autumn. Back-Kaisa, the onetime nursemaid at Mårbacka, who now worked at the loom, was tramping through the woods on her way to the hill-croft where she was born and grew up—on an errand for Lieutenant Lagerlöf. She and little Selma were still great friends, and she had taken the child along. They were in no hurry, these two; they stopped to pick and eat whortleberries growing by the roadside, they admired the gorgeous flybane and gathered their aprons full of lovely mosses to take home with them so as to have something pretty to lay between the inner and storm-windows of the nursery. Back-Kaisa was happy to be once more in the woods, where she knew every shrub and every stone. When they came to the wattled fence which surrounded the clearing where the croft-hut stood and were about to step over the stile, Back-Kaisa said:

"Mind, Selma, you mustn't say a word about war in Father's hearing!"

The little girl was astonished at that. She knew that Back-Kaisa's father was an old soldier who had fought with Napoleon at Leipsic. That one could not speak with him about war seemed unbelievable.

"Why can't I talk to him about war?" she queried.

"That one must never do with them that's been out in a real war," Back-Kaisa told her.

Now the little girl was more astonished than ever. She thought of *Fritiof;* of *Hjalmar;* of *Hector,* and all the gods and heroes of antiquity she had read about in her saga-books—and her head was in a whirl.

In the cabin on the edge of the hearth, with his back to the fire, sat Back-Kaisa's father, a tall, gaunt-looking man with a coarse-featured and furrowed face. That he was of the olden time could be seen by his mode of dress, for he wore knee-breeches and shoes instead of boots and had on a shockingly grimy sheepskin coat. But on the whole his appearance was not more bizarre than that of other old peasants.

The little girl stared and stared at the soldier who would not allow any one to speak of war in his hearing. To her there was nothing so delightful as to hear tales of battles or read stories of wars. She thought it a great pity that she could not ask him to tell her about the things he had been through.

All the while she sat there she dared not speak or reply when spoken to. She felt that if she opened her mouth she would forget, and say something about war, and then the old man might kill her.

After a time she began to think he looked horrible. It was so incomprehensible, this, that one could not talk to him about war. There must be something dreadful back of it all which she did not understand. Perhaps the old man was dangerous? She only wanted to escape, and was ready to make for the door. With every moment that passed her fear increased, and by the time Back-Kaisa was ready to leave and they could at last say good-bye, she was fairly beside herself with fright.

Now, if he had been like other old soldiers, and had said that war was the greatest thing in the world; if he had boasted of killing hundreds of men and burning down whole cities and villages, then the little girl would not have been a bit afraid of him.

VII

THE LAND OF HEART'S DESIRE

IT WAS Lars of London, and Sven of Paris, and
Magnus of Vienna, and Johan of Prague, and Per
of Berlin, and Olle of Maggebysäter, the stableman
and the farmboy!

Now Lars of London, Sven of Paris, Magnus of
Vienna, Johan of Prague, and Per of Berlin, they were
not foreigners, but farm-labourers at Mårbacka.
Lieutenant Lagerlöf, in a facetious moment, had
named his workmen's cottages after the principal cities
of Europe.

Lars of London and Magnus of Vienna had been
plowing all day in the field below the barn; Sven of
Paris had fed the cows and, between times, helped on
the potato land. Johan of Prague had been digging
potatoes, while Per of Berlin, who had been at home all
day nursing a lame back, had come over to the manor
for a little diversion. The stableman had been groom-
ing the horses, and in spare moments chopping
firewood, and the farmboy had worked in the potato
field. Olle of Maggebysäter was not employed at the
farm; he had just come down to Mårbacka to buy a
bushel of rye.

It was a drizzly day in autumn, and the men had gone into the servants' hall for the usual afternoon rest—from half after four to five. Their shoes were covered with mud, their clothing was damp, and they themselves were sour and disgruntled. They had kindled a fire on the hearth, and dropped down round it. Lars of London, who had the largest croft and was the best workman, sat on the chopping-block directly in front of the fire. Magnus of Vienna, who was almost as good a worker as Lars, was sitting next to him, on one of the cobbler's stools. Sven of Paris, who thought himself quite as good as any of them, though he did tend cattle, had planted himself on the edge of the hearth, not caring whether he shut off the blaze from the others. Johan of Prague had taken the other stool and the old man of Berlin had seated himself on a saw-buck just back of the rest. The stableman sat on the edge of the cubby-bed swinging his legs, the farmboy perched on the carpenter's bench, while Olle of Maggebysäter sat down by the door on a barrel of red ochre, resting his feet on his sack of rye.

Lars of London, Magnus of Vienna, Johan of Prague, and Sven of Paris now opened their food-bundles. They each took out a hunk of rye bread with a dab of butter on top. Drawing their sheath-knives from the belts under their leather aprons and wiping them on their trousers, they proceeded to spread their bread and cut it up, bit by bit, eating it in all comfort.

The farmboy was sent over to the kitchen to fetch the fare for himself and the stableman, and came back with two halves of a rye-cake, two pats of butter, and two dishes of cottage cheese. Per of Berlin, not having worked that day, had brought no lunch, and Olle of Maggebysäter had none, either; they just sat and glowered at the others.

When they had finished eating, Lars of London, Magnus of Vienna, Sven of Paris, Johan of Prague, the stableman, and the farmboy simultaneously drew from their trousers' pockets a plug of tobacco. Per of Berlin was not left out on this, for he, too, had his plug; but Olle of Maggebysäter had not even a bit of tobacco in his pocket.

The sheath-knives were again drawn. Now each man cut off a piece of his plug, laid it on his leather apron, chopped it fine, then filled his cutty-pipe.

Lars of London picked up a thin stick of wood and lighted it at the fire. After he had lit his own pipe he gave the light to Magnus of Vienna, who passed it on to Sven of Paris; Sven of Paris handed it to Johan of Prague, who reached back and offered it to Per of Berlin: Per of Berlin leaned over so as to pass it to the stableman, who, after lighting his pipe, held the burning stick in his hand till the farmboy came across the room and took it. Olle of Maggebysäter, to be sure, had no need of a light—having neither pipe nor tobacco. The other men now being warm and well-fed, the world began to look better to them.

But Olle of Maggebysäter was three-score-and-ten, and so crippled with rheumatism that his fingers were stiff and crooked like claws; his head was drawn to one side, one leg was shorter than the other, his sight was poor, his wits were nothing to brag about, and he was toothless and ugly. Washed and combed he had certainly not been in half a year. The fringe of whiskers under his chin was full of sticks and straws. He owned a little croft up in the woods; but being nothing of a worker, he had not been able to keep poverty out of his house. Always grumpy and discontented, he had no friends. And now as the clouds of tobacco smoke rose from the other men's pipes, he muttered, as if to himself:

"I've had nothin' but trouble and misery all my life; but now I've heard about a land they call America, and there I want to go."

The other men sat tranquilly musing over their pipes and made no response.

Olle of Maggebysäter continued:

"You see, 'tis like this in America—you've only to hit a rock with your stick and the rum'll come spurtin' out. That land I want to see afore I die."

The others gazed straight before them and smiled, but said nothing.

Olle of Maggebysäter talked on:

"No one can make me stick at home in this dull, miserable place, when I know there's a land where the hills are full o' rum."

The others remained persistently silent, but not a word of what Olle of Maggebysäter said was lost on them.

"The leaves of the trees in that land, they're nothin' but gold," said the poor old man. "There you don't have to do day's work at a manor, you've only to go to the woods and pull off an armful of leaves, and then you can buy yourself whatever you want. Blow me, if I don't move over there, old as I be!"

They were now in a mellow mood, all the men in the servants' hall. They saw, as it were before their eyes, that land where you tap rum from the rocks and pick gold off the trees.

The farm-bell rang. Rest-time was up. They must again go out into the wet and cold.

Lars of London returned to his plow, Magnus of Vienna to his; Sven of Paris, Johan of Prague, and the farmboy went back to digging potatoes, Per of Berlin betook himself home to his cottage, the stableman had to go and chop the evening's firewood, and Olle of Maggebysäter, shouldering his sack of rye, limped off to the woods.

None of them looked as glum as they did half an hour ago. There was a little glint of light in their eyes. They all felt it was good to know of a land where rum flowed from the hills and the forests were of gold—even though it lay so far away they could never reach it.

VIII

THE "SLOM" SEASON

EAST of Mårbacka, beyond a wooded ridge, lies Gårdsjön, a little lake in which there is a fish we call *slom*. The fish is about two inches long, and so thin as to be almost transparent; but small as it is, it is edible.

In Lieutenant Lagerlöf's time, when everything was so much better than it is now, folks used to take this fish out of the lake in countless numbers. Its spawning time was in early spring, when the ice began to break and there was open water along the shores. One could stand at the water's edge and scoop the fish up with dippers and buckets. Certainly no one went to the bother of putting out nets for slom!

Slom was fished and peddled only at the spawning time; therefore, it was a sure sign of spring when a Gårdsjö fisherman came to the kitchen at Mårbacka with the first catch. The man, knowing he had brought a desired commodity, boldly lifted the latch (in those days there was no lock on the kitchen door) and walked in with an air of confident assurance. He did not stop just inside the door as on other occasions;

without stating his errand, or even saying good-morning, he strode across the floor to the big table and deposited a small basket done up in a blue-checked cotton cloth. Then, stepping back to the door, he stood with head proudly erect, and waited for what was to follow.

If the housekeeper and the maids were the only ones in the kitchen, he could stand a long while unnoticed; for they would not permit themselves to show any signs of curiosity. But if Lieutenant Lagerlöf's little daughters chanced to be there, they were over by the basket at a bound, eagerly untying the cover to see what was under it.

And they found a little porcelain plate, edged round with a blue landscape, which they recognized as having seen every year at this season as far back as they remembered. On the plate was a small mound of slom—some forty or fifty fishes.

Now slom when properly prepared is a tasty fish, but for all that it is considered rather common food. At the other manors in the district it was looked upon as poor man's fare, but not so at Mårbacka. Lieutenant Lagerlöf was such a lover of fish he would hardly eat anything else the year round. After the eelpout had finished spawning, in February, he had to be satisfied with such things as stockfish, dried pike, salt salmon, salt whitefish, to say nothing of the everlasting herring! So every day now he wondered if the slom would be along soon.

The little girls had also learned to regard this fish as a rare treat, and were delighted when they saw what was in the basket. They called to the housekeeper and the maids to come and see. It was slom! Lasse had brought slom! Wasn't it great? Wasn't it wonderful? And there was general rejoicing in the kitchen. The housekeeper immediately went into the pantry and made a sandwich for the fisherman. When handing it to him, she condescended to ask him whether it looked as if there would be a good "take" that year. The fisherman, cocky and self-satisfied (for this was his big day), actually had the temerity to chaff the dignified old housekeeper. He said there would be more slom than all the riches of Lieutenant Lagerlöf could buy.

Mamselle Lovisa, wondering what all this talk meant, came out to the kitchen. Instantly she caught sight of the fisherman and the plate of slom she threw up her hands and exclaimed in despair:

"Good Lord! Is that awful stuff coming in now again!"

It was a great disappointment to the little girls that Aunt Lovisa did not share their delight. Still, she must have had some appreciation of the auspicious event, for she said something in a low tone to the housekeeper, who smiled and nodded approval. Whereupon the children and the maids were told not to let Lieutenant Lagerlöf know the slom had come; it was to be a surprise for his supper.

When the three little girls heard that, they were gladder than ever. Their father was their best friend and playfellow; there was nothing too good for him! They felt very important now, and not for anything would they leave the kitchen. They begged to be allowed to clean the fish, and knew from past years how it should be done: With one stroke you cut off the head, with another you drew out the "innards." The tiny fish had no scales or sharp bones. If you cut off the tail it was a sign you didn't know how slom should be treated. Even after the fishes were cleaned the children would not leave them out of their sight. They watched the housekeeper wash them, dip them in flour, and put them in the frying pan. It wouldn't do to throw slom in the pan just any way. The little fishes had to be laid down very carefully, one by one, close together, none overlapping, and fried hard, so that they all stuck together. Then, with a flip of the pancake-spade, they were turned over. When well browned on both sides, they were covered with a hard round oat-cake, and then turned out of the pan so that the slom lay on top of the bread. The housekeeper told the children that was the way their grandmother had fixed it. In the old mistress's time they used to set before each person at table a round of slom on an oat-cake, for in those days they were not so well off for plates as now.

All the while the slom was frying the children were on pins and needles lest their father should come into the kitchen. Every other minute they ran out in the hall and opened the door to the living room a wee bit to see whether he sat quietly reading his newspaper. When he got up to go for his usual evening walk, their hearts were in their mouths. Oh, dear! What if he should take a notion to go out by the kitchen way——?

Later, at supper, the three little girls could hardly contain themselves. If they but glanced at their father they began to titter. It was hardest for the littlest girl, who had to say grace. In the middle of the prayer she gave a little chirrup like a sparrow when it sees a grain of corn. The Lieutenant was about to ask what had come over her when his eyes fell on the slom right by his plate. His face lit up.

"Thank the Lord we've got something to eat in the house once more!" he said, and actually meant it. For to him only fish was food.

The children after their long silence broke into peals of laughter.

"Oho!" charged the Lieutenant, shaking a finger at them. "So this is why you've been running in and out the whole evening and wouldn't let me read my paper in peace!"

It was an unusually jolly supper. The Lieutenant was always good humoured and talkative, but when he was especially pleased about anything he became quite irresistible. Then he fairly bubbled with amusing anecdotes and kept the whole table convulsed with laughter.

As for the slom, there was no more than the Lieutenant himself could have eaten; but he insisted that all must have a share of this "delicacy." And of course everyone marvelled that such a tiny fish could be so delicious.

"Now, doesn't it taste good, Lovisa?" he asked his sister, who was as fond of meat as he was of fish.

Even she had to concede that just for once like this it was not bad—but too much of it——

When the Lieutenant folded his serviette before rising from table, he said very solemnly:

"Now, children, mind what I'm telling you: The King in his royal palace couldn't have had a better supper than we've had. So we must give God proper thanks for the food and not slur the grace."

Thus ended the first day of the slom season.

The next morning the Gårdsjö fisherman brought a whole pound of slom. He was well met, of course, and he asked twelve *skillings* the pound for his fish, which was considered a high price. The Lieutenant himself came out to the kitchen with the money in order to thank the old man for coming to Mårbacka with the slom, and request him to continue as he had begun.

"Now for pity's sake don't take it to the parson's or the founderer's!" he said.

This time, also, the little girls volunteered to clean the fish. And now they were repaid for their trouble. There was slom enough for the whole family at supper, and some left over for the Lieutenant's breakfast. But the serving-folk did not have any that day, either. It was too choice a dish for them.

The third day the fisherman delivered enough slom to fill a large earthen bowl. Slom was now served at the family table for both breakfast and supper, and in the kitchen it was set before the overseer, but not before the stableman or the farmboy.

The next few days folk from every little hamlet along the lake came bringing slom to Mårbacka. The Lieutenant bought from all. Soon every earthen vessel in the cupboard was filled to overflowing, and the fish had to be emptied into a huge copper kettle; when even that would not hold it all, it was dumped into a big vat.

But to clean such a lot of small fish was no light task! The housemaids had to leave off spinning and weaving to sit in the kitchen cleaning slom. The three little girls were no longer to be seen in the schoolroom. It was not for fun they cleaned slom now, but to help the grown-ups. Fru Lagerlöf and Mamselle Lovisa put aside their other work to give a hand. But it was a bit of a change for them all—a little departure from the usual routine.

The housekeeper did not help clean fish, she stood at the stove the whole day frying it. Before long she began to complain of the quantities of butter the fish was taking. The butter-tub had been full only a few days before, and she could already see the bottom. That was the first break in the general satisfaction.

The family had slom for breakfast and slom for

supper; but thus far at dinner there was the usual
Värmland midday fare—corned beef or pork, or herring-
balls, or fried ham, or sausage, or whatever else there
was on hand.   But such fare was not to the taste of
Lieutenant Lagerlöf.   One day when he was served
meat that had lain in brine since autumn, he lost all
patience.

"I don't see why we should sit here and eat salt food
when the pantry is full of nice fresh fish," he flung out.
"But that's always the way of these fine housekeepers;
they feed the homefolk on salt stuff and let the fresh
things stand on the shelves and spoil—waiting for
company."

That was a sharp rap at his sister.   But Mamselle
Lovisa took it calmly; she was too fond of her brother
to be offended by anything he might say.   She meekly
answered that she had never heard of any one's setting
slom before guests.

"I know, Lovisa, that you are too refined to eat
slom.   You have been out in the great world, and know
how things ought to be.   But I don't see why we back
here at Mårbacka need bother ourselves about what
they do in Karlstad or Åmål."

A light broke in on Mamselle Lovisa.   "But surely
you don't want slom for dinner, too!" she exclaimed,
as if such a thing were unprecedented.

"Certainly I'll eat slom whenever I can get it.   Why
do you suppose I buy it every day, if I'm not to have
any myself?"

After that, they had slom morning, noon, and night; which was not a happy thought on the part of the Lieutenant. There is no denying that slom is a nice-tasting fish, but it has an unpleasant odour. Not in the sense of being tainted; but it is evil-smelling from the moment it comes out of the water. However, all that disappears in the frying. But those who have to handle the raw fish cannot escape, for it is an odour that clings. Do what you will, it stays by you. Everything you touch smells of slom.

Soon all but the Lieutenant began to sicken of slom. They took smaller portions at each meal, and sighed as they sat down at table and saw the everlasting slom set before them again.

Lieutenant Lagerlöf, however, went on buying. The fisherman who had brought the first mess, true to his word, came faithfully every day, and sometimes twice a day. But his manner was noticeably changed. He now pulled the latch-string very gently, and came in with a meek and deprecating smile. He did not set the fish on the kitchen table but left it outside the door. Though he removed his cap and said Good-day, he had to stand and wait a good half-hour before anyone seemed aware of his presence.

Pleasant as it had been for both the maids and the children to escape for a while from the old routine, they were by now so sick and tired of cleaning fish they longed to get back to their regular tasks. None of them would so much as look at the fisherman.

"I say, Lars, you're not bringing slom again to-day, are you?" the housekeeper once asked him, as if he were offering stolen goods.

The man just blinked his eyes; he was too abashed to utter a word.

"We've got more fish now than we can eat," she told him. "I don't believe the Lieutenant wants to buy any more of that horrid stuff." However, she knew the Lieutenant was not to be trifled with in the matter of slom, so of course she had to go in and tell him the fisherman had come.

One day the Lieutenant was out when the old man appeared, so the housekeeper peremptorily ordered him away. All in the kitchen were glad, thinking that for once they would not have to clean any slom. But as luck would have it, the old man met the Lieutenant in the lane; and the latter bought his whole bagful of fish and sent him back to the house with it.

It went on like that for a couple of weeks. Every-one was weary and disgusted—except the Lieutenant. He chanted the praises of slom at every meal; it was wholesome and nutritious food. One need only look at the fishermen down in Bohuslän who lived upon fish; they were the strongest and healthiest men in the whole country.

One evening Mamselle Lovisa tried to tempt him with larded pancakes, a favourite dish of his. And no wonder! for such larded pancakes as the old house-keeper made you never tasted in all your life!

"The overseer and the men, I suppose, must have their fill of slom, so you want me to be satisfied with pancakes." The Lieutenant waved away the plate of nice hot cakes.

"Oh, no, that's not the reason," said Mamselle Lovisa. "The overseer and the men are so sick of slom we dare not set it before them."

Then the Lieutenant had to laugh; but, as he would not touch the pancakes, they had to fetch him his slom.

Toward the end of the second week the whole household was in open rebellion. The housekeeper raged about the inroads on the butter, and the servants declared they could not go on working at a place where they fed you on nothing but slom. It had reached a pass where the Lieutenant dared not show his face in the kitchen; for there the murmurs were loudest. Nor were things as they should be in the dining room. Joy had fled the board. The governess left her plate untouched and the little daughters of the house, who otherwise stuck by their father through thick and thin, even they began to pipe a few feeble protests.

Then at last Fru Lagerlöf came to the rescue. She conferred with Mamselle Lovisa and the housekeeper, and they all thought it time now to resort to the old tried and sure remedy.

At dinner there was boiled slom. Now, the very look of boiled slom is enough! There is a pallor about it peculiarly corpselike, and, besides, it is quite tasteless. Just the sight of it takes away one's appetite.

When the Lieutenant saw the boiled slom he looked as glum as the others.

"We are all out of butter," Mamselle Lovisa gave as excuse; "and since you will have slom at every meal we had no choice but to serve it boiled. For my part," she added, "I think it tastes no worse that way than any other."

The Lieutenant made no answer; so they all knew that Mamselle Lovisa had triumphed. He might easily have stepped into the pantry and seen for himself whether the butter was all gone, or ordered a fresh supply; but he did neither.

After that dinner he bought no more slom. What was the use, he said, when the womenfolk were too lazy to prepare the fish in the proper way? No one contradicted him, though all knew he was as glad as they were to see the last of the slom.

IX

THE SEVENTEENTH OF AUGUST

I

IT IS not easy to say how the seventeenth of August, which was Lieutenant Lagerlöf's birthday, came to be the great day that it was. But one can imagine that with so many gifted persons all living in a little place like East Åmtervik, it was really necessary that they should have a chance, at least once a year, to show what they could do.

When, for example, there were three such fine orators as Engineer Noreen of Herrestad, Senator Nils Andersson of Bävik, and Merchant Teodor Nilsson of Visteberg, the first of whom went in for the pathetic, the second for the profound, and the third for the poetic, it would have been a great pity had they never been heard elsewhere than at small parties and town meetings.

And with a verse writer, too, like Sexton Melanoz at one's command! Days on end he had to sit in the schoolroom and hear the youngsters spell, stammer, and stumble through the intricate mazes of the Swedish language. Surely he needed to let this maltreated tongue ring out in high-sounding eulogistic measures once a year at least!

Then, moreover, there was a male quartette in the parish composed of such good singers as Gustaf and Jan Asker, of the old musical Askers, and the brothers Alfred and Tage Schullström, who kept a store down by the church. People were thankful to them whenever they sang; but for the singers themselves it must have been both stimulating and inspiring to sing at a grand affair where they had critical and discriminating hearers.

And the old man Asker, who played dance music at peasant weddings where nobody cared what came forth from the clarinet just so it had dash and rhythm—he must indeed have been glad to come to Mårbacka on a seventeenth of August! The young folk there appreciated his art, and told him there was no music in the world so easy to dance to as his.

Then, too, there was a brass sextette made up of Tage Schullström, Sergeant Johan Dalhgren, the Gårdsjö Inspector, a shop-clerk and two infant-school teachers. They had all invested in instruments and scores, and had rehearsed marches and waltzes, overtures and folk-songs. It would have been too bad not to have had one gala day, when their efforts were crowned by the award of triumph.

When, besides, among the relatives who spent their summers at Mårbacka there were two clever entertainers like Oriel Afzelius, husband of Fru Lagerlöf's sister, and her own brother, Kristofer Wallroth, it was well that away off here in the farming country there was a fête on a grand enough scale to tempt them to perform.

Moreover, among the guests was a born prima donna, the pretty and merry Stockholmer, Fru Hedda Hedberg, who could act as well as sing, and was in every way adapted for the stage. But she had married a poor Värmland lieutenant. Therefore, one may well say it was almost imperative that there should be a seventeenth of August celebration where all this wealth of talent might come into its own.

II

AFTER Lieutenant Lagerlöf became master of Mårbacka, for the first few years the seventeenth of August was observed in the customary birthday manner; there were flowers on the coffee table and a garland of leaves round the Lieutenant's cup. The neighbours dropped in to wish him many happy returns of the day, and were served with coffee, fruit juice, punch, and toddy. Then came supper at nine o'clock with the usual light chatter. After the meal, tables and chairs were removed from the living room that all might have a bit of a dance.

But somehow it must have been spread abroad that these little birthday parties were rather pleasant affairs. Since there was never any thought of sending out invitations, all who cared to come were welcome; so from year to year more and more folk gathered at Mårbacka.

And there were increases in the families, of course.

As soon as the little ones began to toddle, they had to come along to Mårbacka to celebrate Lieutenant Lagerlöf's birthday. And sometimes the neighbours, who always attended these parties, had guests at home, and, naturally, they brought them.

In those days, when the young gentlemen would go many a mile for the sake of a dance, they, too, began to pay their respects to Lieutenant Lagerlöf on the seventeenth of August. Besides, there were the relatives from other parts of the country who visited Mårbacka every summer, and they planned their trips so as to be present on the Lieutenant's birthday.

As it was always fine weather on the seventeenth of August, in the Lieutenant's lifetime, the guests would while away the time strolling about the grounds, viewing his gardens and buildings. If many young people were present, the dancing would begin before supper. Everyone, no doubt, had a pleasant enough time, though no more so than at other parties.

Then happily Lieutenant Adolf Hedberg and his pretty young wife came to live at East Ämtervik. At Lieutenant Lagerlöf's next birthday party an old peasant woman with a basket of eggs to sell stalked into the kitchen in the midst of the festivities.

She was immediately ordered out, of course; no one had time to stop and buy eggs in the bustle and excitement, with so many guests to be served. Not in the least discouraged, the old woman went round to the veranda, where the Lieutenant sat with a circle of gentlemen. Indeed she was not embarrassed by the presence of the company; her tongue wagged so rapidly and she was so facetiously persistent, he had to buy her eggs to get rid of her. Even after she had stuffed the money into the pocket of her kirtle, she would not go. Then she wanted to know who the other gentlemen were, and commented rather freely on their personal appearance. Finally, young Lieutenant Hedberg, who thought the joke had gone far enough, said:

"You'd better stop now, Hedda."

Whereupon the "old peasant woman" rushed up, and dealt him a sound box on the ear.

"Why, Adolph!" she cried, "how can you be so mean as to give me away like that!"

And indeed it was a shame, for her disguise was so perfect and her Värmland dialect so deliciously natural that none would have taken her for the charming lady from Stockholm.

That bit of drollery set the ball of talents rolling. Along in the evening Kristofer Wallroth sang a number of Eric Bögh's ditties. He had no voice to speak of, but his rendition of the serio-comic was side-splitting. At the end, Auditor Afzelius, with a silk kerchief bound round his head and a mantilla thrown over his shoulder, sang "Emilie's Heart-throbs." That was, of course, the star feature of the evening; the Auditor was inimitable in the rôle of the lovelorn maiden.

It must have been rather galling to the local pride of Sexton Melanoz that only these city folk provided entertainment for the Lieutenant and his guests. But the next year it was the sexton who made the "big hit." The Lieutenant had once presented to the Ottenby school a lot of small wooden muskets made at Mårbacka so that the children might learn to drill. He had even sent an old sergeant to the school to teach the youngsters the first military movements.

The sexton had an inspiration; he and his school children would march to Mårbacka on the Lieutenant's birthday! Shouldering their arms, and led by banner and drum, they came marching along the driveway. It looked as if a whole army were approaching. There were so many the line extended from the manservants' cottage all the way up to the dwelling-house veranda, where the sexton, who was in command, called Halt!

First, he said a few words to the effect that the children had come to thank Lieutenant Lagerlöf for considering that their bodies needed to be developed as well as their minds; then he let them demonstrate how well they could march—do right-about, left-about, close ranks, shoulder arms . . . .

It was a grand surprise the sexton had prepared for them all. The Lieutenant was delighted and his guests were pleased. What the old housekeeper, Mamselle Lovisa, and Fru Lagerlöf thought, when in the middle of a big party they had to serve coffee and cakes to some sixty youngsters, may be left to the imagination. After that, every time the seventeenth of August came round, they remembered with dismay the long procession of children, and hoped the sexton's army would not be so strong this year.

Engineer Noreen and his wife, like the sexton, had felt it was not fair to let folk from outside the parish furnish all the amusement for the seventeenth of August. So along in the evening, when there was a moon, the Engineer donned a black velvet cape and plumed baretta, and Fru Emelie an old-time dress with high puffed sleeves. Then, on the gravel-walk below the veranda, they gave two or three scenes from Börjesson's "Eric XIV." This acting in the mellow moonlight was touched with enchantment. Eric Noreen had so wholly lived himself into the rôle of the unhappy King, it seemed as if every word he spoke came straight from his heart. And Fru Noreen looked sweet and shy and just a bit frightened, as a "Karin Månsdotter" should look.

At the next year's celebration there were more people than ever. Carriages, pony-carts, and chaises came rolling up the avenue. In a short space of time some seventy or eighty persons had arrived. It was evident the report had travelled far and wide that they had many delightful diversions at Mårbacka not to be found elsewhere.

This time the Lieutenant felt quite embarrassed, as there was nothing special to offer the guests. It was just as at any other party; the young folk began to dance in the early afternoon, the *paterfamilias* chatted over their toddy glasses, and the *maters* sat in the drawing

room nibbling fruit and confectionery. Apparently.
no one was bored, for Auditor Afzelius and Dean
Hammargren among the men and Hedda Hedberg and
Nana Hammargren among the women knew how to
enliven a company. The Lieutenant noted no mysterious glances nor any signs of preparation. Not even
the usual birthday speech was forthcoming.

Then as dusk was falling, folk from all the countryside came flocking to Mårbacka. The avenue leading to
the house was soon black with people. The Lieutenant
thought it a pity they had taken the trouble to come
when there was nothing to be seen.

After supper there was a little flutter of excitement
and expectancy among the guests. Presently two
gentlemen placed before the Lieutenant a flower-decked
armchair, and bade him be seated. Instantly strong
arms lifted him on high. Jan Asker struck up a march;
the gentlemen offered their arms to the ladies, and all
marched out into the night. But not for long did they
walk in darkness. When they turned the corner of the
house, the whole garden was a-light with row upon row
of magic lanterns. The Lieutenant was borne along
illuminated walks down to the little park. It was the
first time anything of the sort had been attempted at
Mårbacka. He was struck with wonder and amazement at the beauty of the scene. Could this be the
ground that he and the old gardener had staked and
measured only a few years back?

Exclamations of delight came from all sides. How

dark and mysterious the copses; how deep and endless the paths appeared under their canopy of leaves; how the flowers shimmered and shone in the light of the multi-coloured lanterns; how the masses of foliage hung down from the trees like gorgeous draperies!

The procession halted in one of the glades of the park. The Lieutenant's chair was set down; and, as his dazzled eyes blinked into a grotto of leaves and flowers, Flora, on a pedestal, encircled by little nymphs, sang in a glorious voice a song of praise to the creator of the garden.

"Oh, Hedda!" the Lieutenant cried to the beautiful goddess of flowers, "I might have known that you would not forget me!"

III

IT is about four in the afternoon of a seventeenth of August. The two smaller girls, Selma and Gerda, are dressing for the party. The housemaid pokes her head into the attic storeroom—the room the little girls are occupying temporarily, since their own has been placed at the convenience of visiting relatives.

"Selma and Gerda, you'll have to go down and receive," shouts the maid. "No one else is ready, and the first carriages are coming up the drive."

Now the little girls have to hurry; but at the same time they are thrilled with joy. Just think! It's beginning—the seventeenth of August is beginning!

They button up their frocks, pin on their kerchief

rosettes, and run down. Not a grown person in sight! Not even their elder sister can help them receive, since she is attending a dress rehearsal of the evening's play.

The first arrivals, Herr Nilsson, his wife and four children, are already seated on the veranda. They always come too early to parties, but never so much so as on the seventeenth of August. The little girls do not wonder at that; for everyone must long to come to Mårbacka on such a day.

The time seems a bit long, perhaps, to the guests and their little hostesses before the next vehicle rolls up and the homefolk put in an appearance. But to-day is the Seventeenth, and one does not catch at trifles.

The next arrivals are Pastor Alfred Unger and family from West Ämtervik. They come in a two-horse carriage and have driven about thirteen English miles. The wagon is full of women and children; the parson himself, who is a real horseman, is handling the reins. Lieutenant Lagerlöf, ready at last, comes out on the veranda as the pastor drives in on the grounds.

"Say, Alfred!" he shouts, "what the deuce have you done to your horses? They're as like as two blackberries."

"Chut, chut! You mustn't betray any secrets on your birthday," Pastor Unger shouts back.

As a matter of fact, the parson had two fine carriage horses which would have been exactly alike but for a white spot on the forehead of one of them. He had hit upon the idea of inserting between the blinder-straps of each a piece of white leather, to make it appear that the horses were perfectly matched. No one would have detected the artifice if the pastor had not been so proud of his device that he had talked of it to right and left, and of course the Lieutenant had heard all about it.

But besides this conveyance from West Ämtervik comes a hayrick packed full of young people, relatives from Karlstad. Then wagon after wagon draws up. Here come the Gårdsjö folk—most delightful of guests! They have a long line of vehicles. They are a large family, and besides themselves they have brought Oriel and Georgina Afzelius, and Kristofer Wallroth and his young sister, Julia, who are staying with them.

In one of the Gårdsjö wagons there are some odd looking large white bundles, to be taken upstairs to the theatre. Selma and Gerda are very curious to know what those are for. The little Wallroth girls are sworn to secrecy; all they dare divulge is that Uncle Oriel has thought of something perfectly gorgeous.

Then who should come up but old Engineer Ivan Warberg from Angersby, with a cartful of pretty girls! A jubilant whoop from the veranda! What, a confirmed old bachelor like Ivan Warberg? Who would have thought it! They all know, to be sure, that the girls are his nieces, and his guests for the summer; but they can't resist the fun of teasing Ivan a bit.

The little Lagerlöf girls think it strange Fru Hedda does not appear. True, she no longer lives at East Ämtervik; but they hope she will come and do something jolly. Somehow, it would not be a real seventeenth of August unless she were there.

And now come the nearest neighbours. Pastor Milén and his boys have moved to another parish. To-day, it is the tall, handsome Pastor Lindegren and his sweet little wife who stroll over from the parsonage. From Där Ner in Mårbacka come Mother Kersten and Father Olof; but they are not the only peasant-folk who want to felicitate the Lieutenant. Old man Larsson of Ås, the richest man in the parish, has come with his daughters; the Senator from Bävik with his wife, and the church warden of Västmyr with his.

The little girls are in a perfect twitter of excitement as they stand beside their father and see all who come. One whom they most anxiously await is Jan Asker. They do hope he is not hurt about something and will stay away. They try to count heads, but as people keep pouring in from every direction they soon lose the count. Maybe there are already a hundred guests! They hope it will be a gay party. It sounds so grand to the children when somebody says there were a hundred persons gathered at Mårbacka on the seventeenth of August.

But this receiving is merely an introduction to that which is to follow. It is the same with the coffee-drinking on the lawn. The children wish all such things were over.

Ah, at last it is going to begin! The brass sextette line up in position below the steps. A march is struck.

The gentlemen offer an arm to the ladies and, led by the band, the couples march through the garden down to the little park.

There they gather round a table on which stand glasses of punch and claret-cup. Obviously, the moment has come for the birthday speech and the toast to Lieutenant Lagerlöf. Engineer Noreen, Senator Nils Andersson, and Herr Nilsson of Visteberg have all come prepared to speak. Each wonderingly looks at the others, and hesitates, not wanting to push forward and take the word from his rivals.

"Well, are we to have something?" the Lieutenant asks. These high-flown set speeches are not to his taste, and he is anxious to have that part of the programme over as quickly as possible. Just then from behind him comes a clear voice, with musical Stockholm intonations, and out of the thicket steps a beautiful Zingara. She asks if she may tell his fortune. Taking his left hand between her two pretty hands, she reads the lines of his palm.

Lieutenant Lagerlöf had been very ill during the winter, and to regain his health had spent part of the summer at Strömstad. All his exploits and divertissements on that sojourn the Zingara now reads in his hand, and, moreover, she reveals them in lilting verse.

It is a bit pert and naughty, to be sure, but it provokes laughter and the Lieutenant is charmed.

"Anyhow, you're Number One, Hedda!" he says.

But when Fru Hedda has proposed a health to the

host, and has led the fourfold hurrahs, and the sextette has tooted a fanfare, she gives the three speakers from East Ämtervik a sweeping glance, and says: "Pray, pardon my intrusion. Now it is the turn of the natives."

"The 'natives' are already beaten, Fru Hedberg," replies Engineer Noreen.

Far back in the garden sounds old Jan Asker's clarinet, and the glitter of helmets and shining armour is seen among the trees. Jan Asker and Sexton Melanoz must have come upon three of the Immortal Ases, Odin, Thor, and Freja, who were bound for Mårbacka but had somehow lost their way. Jan and the Sexton have guided them safely hither, so that the shining gods may speak for themselves.

No, they do not speak. The three gods break into song; they chant to the old familiar melody "Come lovely May," a pæan to all that has been wrought here at Mårbacka in the time of Lieutenant Lagerlöf— every word of which is true. Tears glisten in many an eye, and the Lieutenant himself is deeply moved by his old friend's lyric.

"Melanoz is superb to-day!" he says. "After all, Hedda, I believe the natives will carry off the palm."

With this, the fête has been impressively and happily opened. The guests now scatter about the grounds. Some visit the berry bushes and cherry trees, and others want to see whether the fine Mårbacka peaches are ripening.

In a little while comes another fanfare. The gentle-

men now escort the ladies back to the house and up the
perilous attic stairs. The loft has been converted into
a theatre, its small stage screened off with white draperies. The theatre is the work of Fru Lagerlöf, and
is the cutest little place imaginable.

A moment's suspense, and the curtain goes up on a
musical allegory written in the forenoon of that very
day by Oriel Afzelius. It is entitled, "The Monk and
the Dancer." The action takes place on the day of
Lieutenant Lagerlöf's birth, August 17, 1819. Beside
the cradle of the new-born babe, instead of the usual
fairies, stand two symbolical figures, a monk and a
dancer.

The *Dancer* would have the boy grow up a merry,
dashing cavalier. The *Monk*, on the contrary, would
make of him a serious ascetic. After a spirited contro-
versy, they finally come to an agreement. Each shall
direct one half of the little Mårbacka child's span of
life. So for a time he is destined to lead the jolly life
of a young officer; in his later years he is to settle down
quietly, and practise abstinence and good deeds, with
Mårbacka as cloister. Oriel Afzelius as the Monk
and Kristofer Wallroth in draperies and veils as the
Dancer, sing solos and duets from the popular operas.
They gesticulate and declaim with emotional fervour,
and wind up their quarrel with a lively *pas-de-deux*.

As the curtain falls there is wild applause. People
shout, stamp their feet, and wave their handkerchiefs.
Fru Lagerlöf sits in fear and trembling lest the floor

give way under the storm. The Lieutenant cries out: "Yi, yi, Melanoz! It's none of the outlanders winning now!"

The young folk at Mårbacka have rehearsed a little play, but the players feel rather disheartened as they are about to appear; they have nothing to offer comparable to Uncle Oriel's allegory.

Anna Lagerlöf is now fourteen, and this is her first appearance in a regular part. The piece is called "A Cigar," and she is cast for the rôle of the young wife.

Indeed, the performance is far from a failure, thanks to the acting of little Anna Lagerlöf! "How does that child come by her histrionic talent?" people wonder. She acts with such ease, naturalness, and charm, the spectators cannot get over their surprise. "That little girl is going to be a heart-breaker," some are heard to say. "Why, the lass is really pretty!" comes from another quarter. "And how well she acts, too!"

It seemed as if the plaudits and curtain calls would never end.

"Do you see, Lieutenant," shouts Sexton Melanoz above the tumult, "that the natives can hold their own?"

But at last they clamber down the break-neck attic stairs. Then they dance again, and chatter, and drink toddies, and some of them take to story-telling, for which up to then there has been no time.

After supper, at midnight, the Chinese lanterns are lit. This is done every year now, and must never be omitted. For a change, they have the illumination on the front lawn.

Ah! how lovely it looks—as Mamselle Lovisa's flower beds stand out in the vari-coloured light; as the weeping ash, like a huge lamp, sends forth its rays through the lacy branches; as the dark copses gleam as if with fire-flowers!

Now all have come out to see the illuminations. They find themselves in a fairyland. The sweet harmonies of the quartette intensify the spell of enchantment.

Then comes a wonderful thing! It is like the soft caress of a balmy wind. No, one cannot say what it is. But they who have been together these ten hours, chatting, dancing, playing, listening to music and speeches, are now prepared for it. As they drink in the song and the beauty of the night, they are filled with a blissful rapture. Ah, life is so beautiful! How precious the moments! Every breath is a joy!

Now out of the throng steps Fru Hedda. In a moment she appears on the veranda, and starts the Värmland Anthem. All join in the singing, for in this way they are able to express what they feel: *Ack, Värmeland, du sköna, du härliga land!* They seem to hear voices back in the thickets and copses, and surmise that the Mårbacka elves and fairies are dancing a contra-dance under the maple trees to the lovely melody.

Hands press hands; eyes meet eyes through a mist of tears. And no one is surprised, for it is such an unspeakable happiness just to be!

At the close of the song, as Fru Hedda withdraws, Herr Noreen steps forward: he, too, would interpret the spirit of the hour.

"It is *this* that is the seventeenth of August," he says; "not the singing nor the play-acting, not the dancing nor the feasting, but that which we now feel—the sweet solemn joy which has stolen into our hearts, the love which permeates this blessed night. It was for this we longed when we came; it is for this we shall come again next year.

"Why is it, dear Brother Eric Gustaf, that we must come here to you in order to feel reconciled to our fate, proud of our country, happy with ourselves and with those about us? You are no big important man. You have done no great outstanding thing. But you have within you the best of good-will and an open heart. We know that, were it in your power, you would take the whole world in your embrace. This is why you can give us each year a few hours of bliss, a little glimpse of Paradise, which we of East Ämtervik call the Seventeenth of August."

POSTSCRIPT

POSTSCRIPT

I

IT WAS the Seventeenth of August, year 1919.
I had had a wreath bound, the prettiest that
could be made up at Mårbacka, and with this before me in the victoria, I drove to the church. I was
in holiday attire, the victoria shone with a new coat
of varnish, and the horses were in their best harness.

It was a perfect day. The earth lay bathed in sunshine, the air was mild, and across the pale blue sky
floated a few white wisps of cloud. Not the slightest
breeze blew from any direction. It was a Sunday, and
I saw little children in holiday dress playing in the yards,
and grown folk in their Sunday best setting off for
church. No cows or sheep or chickens were seen in
the road, as on weekdays, when the victoria passed
through the village of Ås.

The crop that year was so abundant, it seemed as
if the good old times were back with us again. The
haylofts along the way were so full, shutters and doors
could not be closed; the rye fields were decked with
close rows of shooks; the apple trees in the front yards
hung heavy with reddening fruit, and the fallow fields,
newly sown, showed a tender crop just turning green.

I sat thinking that here was something Lieutenant Lagerlöf—whose centenary it was that day—would have liked to see. Here was prosperity. It was not as in 1918 and 1917 and 1915 and 1914 and 1911— those dreadful years of drouth! How he would have rejoiced at this! He would have nodded to himself, and averred that nowhere in all Värmland could they raise such crops as in his parish.

During the whole long drive to the church, my father was in my thoughts. On this very road he had driven many and many a time. I pictured with what keen interest he would have noted all the changes. Every house which had been repainted, every new window, every roof where tiling had replaced the old shingles, he would have pointed out and commented upon. The cottage Där Fram at Ås, which had remained unaltered, would have delighted him; but he would have been sorry to find Jan Larsson's old house—the finest in the parish in his time—torn down.

Certainly he had never been opposed to changes and improvements, though there were some time-honoured things he had wished to leave undisturbed. Were he here now, he would think us a shiftless lot to have in this day and age the old crooked, sagging fences that were here in his time. He would be shocked to find the road ditches still choked with weeds, the bridges weak and full of holes, and the dung-yards still lying at the edge of the road.

When I came to the crossing where the village road

runs into the great highway, how I wished I might have pointed out to him the fine health resort among the hills, and told him that Ås Springs were now visited every year by hundreds of people. It would have gladdened him to know that his idea—that this would some day be a popular watering-place—had not been so far afield. I could have wished he were beside me in the carriage as I drove across the Ämtan Bridge! It would have been a joy to show him that the river had at last been dredged, and now ran in a straight course, no longer overflowing its banks.

As I drove by the Ostenby school, I seemed to see him standing on the playground scattering handfuls of pennies—happy and content as always, when he had a crowd of children about him. I had heard him say, time and time again, that popular education was a calamity, and would bring us to ruin. But all the same, on every examination day, he would drive down to the school to sit for hours while his good friend Melanoz quizzed the children in catechism and history, and let them show how clever they were at arithmetic and composition. I doubt whether there was any one more pleased than he when the youngsters gave correct answers and got good marks and prizes. I had often wondered at this; but now I understand that where children were concerned, all prejudice was thrown to the winds.

I remembered how it had been in the old days when we drove into the church grove. We were hailed with cheery salutations as folk sprang aside to let our carriage pass, and father sat smiling and raising his hand to the brim of his hat. But when I drove in on the same ground, the place looked so empty and deserted.

I was alone in the carriage, and among all who had come to the church only I remembered that this was my father's birthday. I stepped out and went over to the churchyard to place the wreath. My sad heart wept over my loved ones who lay sleeping there. Father and Mother, Grandmother, Aunt Lovisa, and the old housekeeper—I had seen them all laid away.

I longed for them, I wished they might come back and dwell in that Mårbacka which their labours had built up.

But still, silent, inaccessible, they slept on. They seemed not to hear me. Yet, perhaps they did. Perhaps these recollections, which have hovered round me the last few years, were sent forth by them. I do not know, but I love to think so.

THE END